Joe Sails

A story in progress

Lone Tree Publishing Inc.
5572 War Admiral Road
Virginia Beach, VA 23462-4044

Published 2004
2nd Printing

ISBN: 0-9724117-1-2

Lone Tree Publishing Inc.
5572 War Admiral Road
Virginia Beach, VA 23462-4044

"Hats off to Olenych for a job well done!"

Chuck Hamsa
Reviewers Consortium

"The author's professional yet friendly writing style makes for an incredibly fast and smooth read for every academic level..."

Denise M. Clark
Author / "A Man's War"

"...watch out Ken Blanchard. There is a new author about."

Brefi Group
United Kingdom

"Every business culture requires a strong foundation. Joe Sails A Story in Progress is the brick & mortar."

John V. O'Neil / President
Sales Success, Inc

"...it trains the reader to become a more effective worker and communicator..."

Kathryn Lively
Author / " Saints Preserve US"

Table of Contents

Introduction

This story is for all of those managers that are stuck in a process of diminishing returns. Running an organization by numbers alone is like having an engineer run marketing. There has to be a complimentary way of managing towards results while serving your employees and company better.

The intrinsic nature of sales with personalities and relationships makes it a very difficult process to neatly define and shove into square little boxes. Even though our management culture dictates that we manage for results, we often lose focus on the real elements of selling. We value skill sets, but overlook core competencies. This book is the first step in getting back to the basics. Not the basic sales skills, but the basis of core competencies. If you are lucky enough to be mildly successful in elevating core competencies your employees will benefit and your company will flourish.

While this book revolves around a salesperson it is an allegory for everyone in business. Note some of the non-sales characters and you'll see how important core competencies are in everyone's job.

I've been one of those managers and I've been stuck in the flow of information up the ladder and down the ladder. It was while I was trying to mandate change that this book evolved. I was trying to force change on others without their sincere buy-in.

Please use this book as a benchmarking tool to evaluate yourself and your organization. It doesn't matter what you sell, this book will help you begin the process of changing core competencies in a non-abrasive manner that elicits ownership and commitment.

Chapter 1

ship wrecked

"Hey, Louise, how was your weekend?"

"Great Joe," bubbles Louise the front desk receptionist/office administrator/regional coordinator. Louise has been with Acme for only 14 months and has been given more responsibilities as other Acme employees have left the company. She sees it as a challenge that may help her later. If nothing else the new activities make the days go by faster, especially now that everyone has cell phones, voice mail and email.

Joe likes her a lot more than all the other support people that have come and gone in this office. He feels that her gung - ho attitude is a little much, but he figures that it was probably due to her being younger than he is. You see, Joe has been around Acme for over eight years and sees himself as the senior salesperson. He has been in the trenches as a named account executive longer than anyone else. He knows he knows more than anyone, but being "Mister Positive" in this environment is not something that he can do. Every day is too much of a challenge! It's getting harder and harder in the field and it never seems to get easier inside of Acme. Now, he doesn't even have his system support engineers to help him with his email.

It is Monday morning and Joe dumps his briefcase at his desk on the way to the coffeepot. Just outside the break room he runs into Bills, Bill Hamilton. Joe calls Bill Hamilton "Bills" because of all of the money he has. It's rumored that he bought a new house in Wercforit Estates. Bills is a couple of years older than Joe and transferred in from another region as the area manager about three years ago. Last year he was re-assigned to a named account executive position because of the sales force reduction. It didn't seem to affect him too much. He's the number two salesperson in the region for the first half, right behind Melissa. "Hey, Bills, where are you off to this fine Monday morning?" Joe asks.

Bills replies in a rush, "I can't talk now I'm on my way to a breakfast meeting with the field service engineers."

In a panic Joe cries, "No one told me about a Monday morning meeting!"

"I've been meeting with a different service team every two weeks or so since I was transferred. Normally, I'm at the start of the 7:30 meeting, but I asked them to begin it without me today. I wanted to come in and check out the demo room. Care Free Leisure is coming in on Wednesday and I wanted to make sure we still had the new multifunctional 752F on the floor. You know with the way that Corporate is mandating to rotate our demonstration equipment, you always have to triple check."

"Why do you meet with the service people every couple of weeks?" questions Joe. "They call whenever there are persistent problems with the equipment. Lately I haven't gotten any calls, so they must be doing a great job."

Bills, "I don't meet with them to talk ONLY about

service issues, I also discuss what is happening in the field with them and our customers. They're a wealth of information. It was because of Corie Wratchet that I got this demo on Wednesday. I had called the purchasing person at Care Free Leisure just three weeks ago and everything seemed fine with their old box. They said they were not in the market."

"Then Corie tells me a week ago while she was on a routine service call that she heard Paul, the production manager bragging about a big print job they just won. Well, you can imagine how fast I jumped on that. I immediately went on the Net and researched their company some more. Heck, I even got a new D&B profile for them and within two days had a meeting with Paul. The meeting went well and I've been back with Tom (the local system support engineer) to look at specific needs. It certainly isn't a closed deal, as a matter of fact; I would say that this is really not a demonstration, but rather an Acme overview with some equipment thrown in. Look, Joe I've really got to go. Have fun in Happy Valley."

"Yeah, right. Let me know how your demo goes. Good luck," Joe replies. Joe watches Bills hurry out the door. Joe can't help but think that Bills is one of the luckiest guys he knows.

Joe finally enters the break room and notices that the coffeepot is empty.

He decides it isn't that important and heads back to his desk where his briefcase has fallen to the floor. He didn't have time earlier to zip the pocket and his papers are scattered on his chair and the carpet. He moans, "Another Monday," and gathers his papers and planner.

He picks up his black leather case and retrieves his laptop from the middle compartment. He had actually won this briefcase three or four years ago? He was the top copier salesperson on the team for the quarter and he won this black, Acme embroidered briefcase. It was either the briefcase or a brown satchel. The briefcase is OK, but not as nice as the new ones with the compartment for your PDA. Joe tries to think if it is the last prize he won. He realizes that his mind is wandering and decides to get down to business. It's 8:49 and he picks his phone up to see if there are any messages. He is relieved to find only two messages from Friday afternoon and one from today. He hits his message button and starts listening to the first one. After just a few seconds his knuckles turn white and he moans again before he slams the phone down.

The message was from Jack at the warehouse. He said that he wasn't going to be able to deliver that 418SF today because the sorter never shipped. Great, another supply chain problem, Joe thinks. They just never seem to get it right. "Can't anyone do anything right around here!" he yells. He marches right into his manager's office at the end of the cubicles. On the walls are the familiar pictures of a golf course and a crewing team with the ALL too positive statements - team work allows everyone to win and challenges are meant to be overcome.

Bobbi is Joe's manager. She is definitely a different manager than Bills. Her style is more like his old high school coaches and less like a corporate manager. She can motivate you and will listen to your problems, but she wants results. At only 5' 2", she has proven time and time again that she is no one to tussle with. She's demanding of herself and has recently started turning up the heat on Joe to get more activity. And now with this new EBAY or EBDAY stuff, Joe knows she'll be wanting more. Joe doesn't know where those results will come from. His territory has always been very competitive and his customers always shop around for the best prices. That is a fact and management is just going to have to understand it. He works hard enough as it is and he certainly can not do any more. Joe's favorite saying is, "You can't get blood out of a turnip." The real problem is getting equipment delivered. They CAN'T do anything right.

Bobbi pulls Joe back to his reality by asking, "Forget to set your alarm, Joe?"

"Oh, I, huh… you know how bad traffic is in the morning." He lets Bobbi's comment slide without much of a defense. He left his house at 7:45 this morning. He can't be responsible for rush hour traffic. It's not his fault that this wonderful city could not plan the roads any better. "Hey," he continues, " I didn't come in here this morning to talk about traffic. I have a problem that YOU need to fix."

Bobbi has been through this scene a couple of times before with him and knows that by the end of the conversation, Joe will be settled down and focused on other "problems." She has tried for some time now to get Joe to take greater ownership of his days. A couple of times she has seen a sliver of change, but when something goes wrong it always comes back to someone else. She has tried to give him suggestions, but he likes to think of himself as an "old salt" even though he just recently celebrated his thirty-second birthday. All of those suggestions have gotten the same reply, "You can't get blood out of a turnip." There must be a way for her to make him more productive.

Joe rants for five minutes about the equipment delivery problems and that if they were fixed he would be at plan or better, before Bobbi asks, "OK, Joe what is OUR issue today?"

He finally gets to his 418SF not shipping on

Friday. "I promised All Square Construction that it would be there, and now I pick up a message today saying that it wasn't delivered. They are going to be really mad and I may lose the business. You know how long I've been working on this one. How can I make my plan when everyone around me keeps screwing up?"

Bobbi interjects quickly, "Settle down, Joe, I'll call Jack and find out what happened. What has the customer told you so far?"

Joe's defenses go up and he says he hasn't talked to the customer yet. He wants to have a definite delivery time before he calls them.

As Joe walks out of Bobbi's office he can hear her say, "You shouldn't let this stuff affect you so much. The supply chain isn't out to get you. It's an issue that we're...."

Joe doesn't hear the rest. He has heard it all before. He walks past his teammates' cubicles. They're all empty.

He decides that now may be a good time for that cup of java. Joe slams his shoulder into the door. It swings open easily under his weight. Once again the pot is empty. "Oh well, I've got bigger things to do than make a pot of coffee," he muses.

Back at his desk, he turns on his computer and connects using the fastest technology available, one step above carrier pigeons. He waits looking at his blank screen. What's he going to do for the rest of the day? He tries to remember if his plan and review is today or tomorrow. He knows he has that initial call late this afternoon at Carroll's Food and Beverage Wholesalers. He can't remember if it is at one or two. His desktop appears and his computer is finally ready to go.

He punches the keys and gets to Lotus Notes to check his mail. Nothing from his bosses. He decides to read the other stuff later. Lately, later has been never.

His screen is mostly a sea of red, which means the emails haven't been opened. There are a few emails that have been opened, but even those haven't been fully read. Who has the time for all of this information overload? He figures all he needs is the spec sheet and the price. If anything comes up during the sales cycle, he'll get special pricing from Bobbi. This EBADUH stuff isn't going to be around forever. (EBITDA - Earnings, Before Interest, Taxes, Depreciation and Amortization. Phase-one of Acme's new compensation model was just beginning to rollout to the field. The sales organization was now tasked with ensuring that every deal had adequate profit margins in it. Goals were not based just on projected revenues. The sales force now had two targets to achieve in Phase-one, revenues and profit or EBITDA.) And besides, he had that five-unit fax order at the beginning of the year that was way above cost. It wasn't his fault the system support engineers took three days to install them on the customer's network. "Now I can't even offer free installation with my equipment," Joe gripes.

He sits there in his cubicle debating with himself if he should call All Square Construction and test the customer's reactions or let a sleeping dog lie. He eventually decides against calling and instead calls to confirm his appointment for Carroll's Food and Beverage Wholesalers. Kelsey, his contact, picks up after just one ring then pleasantly and professionally does her introductions. Joe feels lucky because Kelsey is normally hard to get a hold of. She does confirm their appointment for one, but explains that she will not be the only one he'll be meeting with. "There will actually be three or four of us meeting with you."

"Great," Joe replies enthusiastically, "the more the merrier. I'll see you at one."

He replaces his phone and notices that it's already

10:30. If only he could find more time. The days just seem to be one problem after another. There's never enough time for my real job - selling. He thinks back to his glory days, when he was at plan and things were great with the company. Back then he could sell Rogaine to Robin Williams. At one point, several years ago he even sold a customer an additional copier just for back up. The customer had placed it in their maintenance closet and would roll it out when the primary unit needed repairs. It didn't quite work out as planned though, because an employee was making copies of his or hers asstribute and sending the images to the owner. They never did find the person. But they did cancel the extra machine.

Joe mutters, "I might as well listen to the rest of my messages." Once again he starts to listen to Jack explain the NON-delivery. Joe saves the message just in case he needs to forward it to Bobbi later. It may come in handy if he loses the order. The second message was dated at 2:56 on Friday and it was from Rod Stoneworth - the owner at All Square Construction.

"Joe, its Rod, please give me a call. The machine hasn't arrived yet and some of my people leave at three. You know the number. Thanks."

"Hmmm... I guess I could call him, but I have nothing to say," Joe thinks. "I'll wait until I hear back from Bobbi."

The last message that he retrieves is from his regional sales director, and it's dated Monday 7:45am. "Joe, this is Bishop. Give me a call today; I want to discuss a focus group that Corporate is putting together on some of the equipment delivery issues. Since you're the most vocal, I figured you would jump at this chance to help improve the system. I'll be on my cell today the number is...." Joe wants nothing to do with any focus group. Just then Bobbi approaches. Joe hangs up. He'll call Bishop back later with some excuse NOT to participate.

"Bobbi, did you fix it?" Joe asks.

Bobbi nods and says, "Yeah, Jack told me that the unit should be arriving this morning. They found the sorter Friday afternoon. I guess it was there the whole time. They had stored it with the wrong mainframe. It wasn't a big issue after all. Let me know what this customer says, OK?"

"Sure not a problem Bobbi," Joe says. Joe is just about ready to thank her when his phone rings and he turns to answer it. This effectively terminates his conversation with Bobbi.

"Joe here," he automatically says.

"Ah, is this Acme?" a shy voice on the other end of the phone asks.

"Yes, it sure is the last time I checked," Joe's reply is robust.

"Ah, my name is Stephen and I got this number from our files. I was hoping I could talk to someone about our machine...."

Joe interrupts and asks, "Is it broke?"

"Uh, yes sir it is," Stephen eagerly offers.

"Oh well, you'll need to call our service folks. They're the best. Got a pen Steve? Great, dial 800 AOK-ACME."

"800 AOK -ACME?"

"Yeah, just dial 1-800 A O K - A C M E. You know spell it out on your phone's number buttons. You do have a push button phone don't you, Steve?" Again Joe chuckles a bit too loud.

Steve quickly thanks him and calls yet another Acme number.

Joe decides to wait until after his afternoon

meeting to call All Square Construction. No reason to get yelled at now. I'll wait until I'm sure their box has been delivered. It's only a couple more hours and hopefully they won't be as mad then.

I better get going, if I'm going to grab lunch before my one o'clock meeting. Joe turns off his computer and gathers his stuff before arranging his briefcase. On the way out he looks to see if there's any coffee. Bingo, he's in luck. It looks to be fresh pot. Maybe my luck is changing, Joe thinks. He looks around for one of those small white Styrofoam cups. After a moment or two of looking, he locates the stash of four sleeves in a cupboard over the refrigerator. After tearing the thin plastic, he grabs one cup and leaves the rest of them in their hiding place. He pours himself a cup and relishes the flavor. "Boy, I sure could have used this earlier," he thinks.

At his favorite eatery, The Deli, he finds a seat in the back. After ordering ham and cheese on rye (everyone at the office thinks the breads here are the best) he grabs the local sports section of his paper and waits. He notices that his high school team is about to start a new season. The local school board did some redistricting a couple of years ago and his team hasn't been able to get on a winning streak since. His old coach is quoted, "Without the big men in front, we can't run the ball like we used to on the power plays. So, this year we're changing our strategy, we'll be running more option plays and throwing the ball more. We're going to challenge our competition in their end zones."

To Joe, it was just another way of saying that they're going to have another losing season.

In front of him is, by all accounts, a huge ham and cheese sandwich with just the right amount of mustard to tang each bite. To say it's delicious would be an insult.

Joe digs in and savors every bite, a thing of beauty shouldn't be rushed.

Twenty minutes after lunch Joe is in the lobby of Carroll's Food and Beverage Wholesalers with fifteen minutes to spare. As he walks up to the receptionist, he smiles and pleasantly asks for Kelsey Opportern. The receptionist asks if he's from Acme then she informs Joe that Ms. Opportern is expecting him and would he like to have a seat. Joe thanks her and walks toward the trophy case passing all of Carroll's Food and Beverage Warehouse's company information, which includes a brief history, the latest annual report, directory and catalogs. Joe looks for some names on the trophies for anyone he may know. "You never know maybe there's a contact in there somewhere," he thinks.

Joe whirls around when he hears the clicking of heels on the polished tile floor. Ms. Opportern is of medium build with a professional blue pinstriped suit on. She warmly extends her hand and introduces herself. "Hi, I am Kelsey Opportern. I'm glad you could make it."

Joe enthusiastically shakes Kelsey's hand and responds, "Thanks for seeing me, Kelsey. You seem to have a nice place here."

"Thank you. I hope it was no trouble getting here?" she inquires.

"No, not at all. I actually live only a couple of miles from here. Do you know where Brier Homes are?" Joe continues to talk about his house and neighborhood until they reach the conference room. Kelsey seems very personable and Joe thinks he's established a rapport with her.

Joe is seated at very large cherry conference table. Boy, this must have cost more than my salary he mindfully calculates. Just as Kelsey settles into the seat across from him, the door opens again and in stroll two men. They greet Kelsey and extend their hands to Joe. Joe is introduced to Michael and Preston. Michael takes a seat next to Kelsey. On the other side of the table Preston sits at the head of the table. The meeting begins.

Joe has been in so many initial meetings that he could do it in his sleep. He starts, "Thanks for your time. My name is Joe and I am your Acme sales executive. Acme is an office equipment company that focuses on integrating the best copiers from our partners, to give you the solutions that you need. We compete very aggressively with the industry leaders."

A short time later his inquisition begins, "What type of equipment do you use today? Is it on lease or do you prefer to buy it outright? Do you have any special requirements like - going digital? In my professional opinion," grouses Joe, "you'd be stupid NOT to go digital."

After more than an hour of similar questions Joe has captured three pages of notes about their copiers and faxes. It seems to be a great first call. Joe's sitting in his car and its almost 2:30. He is mentally reviewing the call and calculating if he can ultimately win this one. He's sure he can. They hate their current vendor. Well, they didn't actually say they hated them. They said they were looking at alternatives. To Joe, that means that the other guy blew it and now it's his turn. Lets see I'm at the right level - Kelsey is in purchasing. Oh, I should ask her what Michael's and Preston's titles are. One of them asked that network question, "Do your products run on NT?" Joe assumes then that they must be network administrators or something.

He felt he nailed his reply, "Our system support engineers are the best in the business. They can make our products work in virtually all environments. We can make your documents sing!"

Now what to do? He could go back to the office and then fight the traffic home or maybe he would do some cold calling in this part of town. Get some things going and then head home. He could walk in his front door at a reasonable hour. But, before he starts he needs to check voice mail one more time.

"Joe, this is Rod Stoneworth. Our machine finally got here today, please give me a call."

The second message is from Bobbi, "Hey Joe, did you see that we made our EBITDA goals for the second quarter? Good news - huh? I'm really calling to confirm our P&R tomorrow at 3:00. Please give me a call. Oh, by the way I've got an idea that may help both of us."

Joe rifles through the rest of his voice mail and then decides to call Bishop about the task force. He reaches in the back of his Sedan and retrieves his suit jacket. There in the breast pocket is his Palm. Within just a couple of seconds he has dialed the main number to the regional office. A pleasant recording apologizes for any inconvenience and assures him that a customer support staff member will help him shortly. The Muzak is interrupted a few moments later.

"Hey Kevin, this is Joe. Is Bishop in today?"

Kevin says, "Sorry Joe, Bishop is out of the office."

"Do you know where he is today? If he's at the district office I'd like to get that toll-free number. I'll call him from a land line. My cell bills are sky high."

Kevin inquires, "I didn't know you had a cell phone. Let me update the regional directory, OK?"

"Uh, well, uh, Kevin I don't give it out. Uh, no one in Acme knows the number because it's just too expensive to talk on it all day long. I, uh, only use it in emergencies like now," Joe stammers.

"Sure, Joe I understand. I just talked to Bishop a couple of minutes ago and he's in his car. Do you want me to connect you with his cell?" Kevin asks.

"Sure, thanks."

A couple of minutes later Bishop gets on the phone, "Hey Joe, I'm glad you called. How have you been?"

"You know me Bishop, busy, busy, busy."

"I just hope that you're selling profitable business, not those low margin deals that don't make us any money," Bishop states.

Joe responds, "Bishop, I wish you were with me today, I just came from a great opportunity. I'll be putting it in the 'Forecaster' as soon as I can catch a minute." The "Forecaster" is a software program that resides on every salesperson's computer. It allows for suspects, prospects and current sales cycles to be added, so that managers above Joe could see what he was delivering. Joe had heard all the logic behind how important the software was at least a trillion times, but he could never really shake the feeling that BIG BROTHER was watching his every move. It never really used to bother him that THEY were watching, but because the last couple of quarters were dismal he has been very conscience of everything that he has typed into the "Forecaster." So the "Forecaster" is the tool that Acme uses to track the sales cycles of each individual. It should figuratively look like a pyramid with the wide base representing the prospect/suspects that a salesperson has and the point being the orders that will close for that month. On the one hand he doesn't want to put things down that aren't real, but on the other hand he has to put something down. It's the cardinal rule to forecast your budget every month or the head honchos go bonkers.

"Good," Bishop comments and then changes gears with, "I'm excited to have you on this new taskforce. I know you've been discussing with Bobbi our equipment delivery issues. We could sure use your, umm, uh, passion."

Joe chooses his words carefully, "Hey Bishop, I would really like to help, but I've got so much going on in my territory that I don't think I can break away. I'm your man who brings in the bacon. I'm not good at being a committee delegate. And besides, I've got a lot of things going on at home too. I just don't think I can give any more."

Bishop's disappointment is evident, "We could really use you Joe. Just do me a favor and give me a call next week after you've had some time to think about MY request."

"Sure, sure, Bishop whatever you say. I'll see you later." Joe punches the end button and begins to feel trapped and a little teed-off that he's going to be forced into this. "What a jerk," he mutters.

He shakes his head and thinks. I would like to see any manager or director do what I do. They're all just overhead. If it weren't for the sales force and people like me in the trenches this company wouldn't be anywhere! Maybe the next time Bishop would like me to kiss his ring. He starts to look for the phone number for All Square Construction.

"Rod, this is Joe from Acme. How's my favorite customer today?" Joe's old line sounds practiced and insincere.

Rod Stoneworth has built his construction company from scratch. Twenty years earlier he was a new, bungling carpenter without a tool belt to hang his hammer on. Today, All Square Construction company builds residential and commercial properties and sells over $15 million of properties a year. But their real revenue comes from their ongoing real estate ventures. The profits from their annual leases are twice that from the construction side. If Joe had asked he would have learned that Rod recently bought one of the largest local real estate companies in the city. Joe never asked.

Rod did not build a successful company by overreacting. He judges people on what they show him, not what they say. And at this rate Joe has two strikes against him. Strike one - no communication after his call on Friday. Strike two - no apology. He'll give Joe one more chance to redeem himself.

Rod inquires, "Joe, I thought the machine for my Valley location was going to be delivered on Friday at 2:00. What happened?"

"Rod, I never got the call from the warehouse until today and uh, you got it, though today, right?"

Strike three. Joe did not take ownership of the problem or worse he had just lied.

"Joe, just keep in touch with Julie my administrative assistant will you? I've got to go. Thanks for everything." And with that Rod said good-bye for the last time. Rod has been around long enough to realize when someone is trying to cover himself from blame.

Boy, that wasn't too difficult thinks Joe. That Rod is a nice guy. I'll surprise him in a couple of weeks and see if he wants to go to lunch, my treat.

Wow, it's already 3:00. I guess I could go back to my house and return some calls. Where does the day go! I'm so busy, but I never get anything done. "What do I need to do to be more productive?" Joe thinks out loud.

Chapter 2

proposal

Bobbi's stumped. She has not been able to motivate Joe since she got here. The first month she was here nearly a year ago Joe had some great results, but ever since then his contributions have definitely fallen off. The pep talks haven't worked and the little jabs like the one yesterday about his alarm clock seem to go right over his head. She realizes that Joe is bringing down the performance of her team and he either has to begin to produce or she will have to find someone else.

The second option will certainly affect her results for the next couple of quarters because of training and acclamation issues with a new hire. Her real concern though is if she terminates Joe then there is a chance that the company may not allow her to backfill his position. That would mean additional territory and budget for her other sales people. She feels that her team is already spread thin and that any further reduction in headcount will be counter-productive. Maybe she could ask Bishop for some insight. No, she quickly changes her mind on that idea. Why make yourself look like you don't know what you are doing? She'll try a different approach this time with Joe. She's not sure exactly what it will be, but it has to be substantially different than reviewing prospects and deals. The "Forecaster" hasn't seemed to help. She must actively monitor his progress on a more rudimental level. She feels discouraged because if she can't effectively manage a group of eight salespeople how will she ever become a regional sales director? Joe is her challenge, and she is committed to righting him. She thinks that is actually a very good description.

Joe is a ship that is a little off course; well the truth of the matter is, he's a lot off course. And he's taking on water, which is causing him to list to one side and further him from his true course. Bobbi embellishes further this comparison by adding that unbeknown to Joe, there is a typhoon over the horizon that could sink him. But, what does she do first, repair all of the leaks, bail water, change course, or get a new captain? With limited resources, there is only so much that can be done to improve Joe and his core behavior or competencies. The familiar chirp of her cell phone shakes her from her analogy and she realizes that changing Joe will take all of her efforts.

A plan is forming in the depths of her subconscious and hasn't made it to the surface. She knows the direction she must take for Joe's transformation, but the details are vague.

"Good morning, this is Bobbi Dunham, sales manager for Acme, how may I help you?" she rhythmically says into her Sanyo.

"Hey Bobbi, it's Joe, how are you?" Joe absently asks.

"Good Joe, I hope you are doing well." She immediately takes the initiative (her retraining efforts of Joe begin) and continues, "Bishop called me yesterday afternoon and said that you..."

Joe interrupts her and starts to object about having to be on some silly-ass supply chain committee, when Bobbi firmly states, "Joe settle down." She pauses for effect and then continues more gently, "Joe, we talked primarily about your newest prospect and the hope we both have that it will be a good opportunity for you." Actually they had also talked about the equipment delivery committee, but she was not going to brow beat Joe with that topic just yet. And she certainly wasn't going to let Joe continue to flounder. She was going to lead by example, but first she had to get Joe to let her.

"I need to focus on some core customer issues and I want to do that by being customer focused. I obviously cannot engage every account that Acme has, so I'm choosing one suspect and following them through our cycles and defining what is working and what's not. I would like to review this new opportunity as a personal challenge for me. I'm sure I'll learn a lot about Acme's strengths and weaknesses. Furthermore, I'm sure I'll learn a lot about selling from you."

Joe cautiously responds, "Look Bobbi, I think that's a great idea, but I haven't even entered the information into the "Forecaster" yet. It looks good, but I would hate for you to waste your time. Isn't there any other account you could find to be your guinea pig?"

Bobbi had anticipated this response because it was just so, Joe. "Well, I guess I could call another account. What was the account's name from the delivery issue last Friday? I'll call them up or maybe you and I can spend a day with them going over Acme's strengths."

"I don't think that would be a good account either because they're real finicky about vendors and I have such a good relationship that I would hate to upset the apple cart at this point," Joe squirms.

Bobbi knows she has to press him or he'll just give her more lip service. "Joe, this delivery problem is a big issue within ALL of our accounts. I'll just ask Jack to give me the point of contact information from the delivery schedule and I'll let you know how I'm doing."

Joe does not want her snooping around any of his accounts where he may be at fault. "Please listen to me Bobbi, this isn't the right account, but maybe Carroll's from yesterday would be better. Yeah, I think you were right with the first suggestion. I'll keep you informed of all developments as they happen," Joe comments. He feels like he has dodged another bullet.

"Ok Joe, it's your territory. I'll be focused on the Carroll's account. I can't wait to learn from you, but I'll be active in the account. How about we go over your initial call with them during our plan and review this afternoon?"

"Yeah, sure no problem. I'll see you at three," Joe responds.

It's already 10:00 in the morning and Joe is walking out of his first appointment into a cloudy, drizzling day. He just hasn't quite gotten into the groove, though. His appointment went well, but he doesn't believe it will amount to too much. He had sold this customer some small copiers a couple of years ago and they are not really in the market for anything now. His contact has even left them, so he'd have to start from scratch, which is always a long, time-consuming effort. He should have asked where she went, but it doesn't matter because there's probably nothing there either.

He tried to jump-start his productivity by having an 8:00 o'clock appointment. He figured that if he could do that every day for a month that would be twenty more customer calls. He should be able to get some more sales that way. The issue will be leaving his home by 7:25 every morning.

Once in his car, Joe picks up his cell phone to check his voice mail. While the phone is wedged between his shoulder and his ear, Joe reaches for the super gonzo-size coffee cup. It's still warm and seems to hit the spot. Not much new with the first couple of voice messages. The first is from Bobbi reminding him of their P&R. The next one is from service about a machine problem and the final one is a blue bird. The customer, Army National Guard, currently has a competitive machine and may want to replace it. Joe thinks that he could make it over to their address before lunch, but he really should be trying to clear up that billing issue.

He knows he has to go over to One Price Quality Cleaners and try to resolve their service billing problems. Boy, he hates always having to do other people's work. Why can't Acme just get the right bill to the right person? Why does he have to go out to verify the serial number and meter reads? He begrudgingly admits to himself that he may have initially screwed up the order form when the unit was placed last year. If he remembers correctly, it was because of that new promotion with the three months of free service. So he had to re-submit the form. If he didn't, he would not have captured that additional margin and would not have gotten his fair pay. It is just so frustrating to work on these billing issues. This is really administration's work and he doesn't get paid for it.

He decides that he is a salesperson and thus he will do a quick surprise visit to this new suspect and impress them with his responsiveness. If he has time after lunch and before Bobbi's "interrogation", he'll get over to OPQC (One Price Quality Cleaners).

"Where's that map?" Joe mutters as he takes another gulp of coffee. He switches the cup from his right hand to his left as he stretches to reach under the passenger seat. He keeps his eye on his new coffee hand as he leans over to the right, so that he won't spill. He feels a little jolt of elation when his right hand retrieves the City Road Book and he has once again maneuvered back into an upright position.

"With moves like that I should be in the Hall of Fame," Joe chuckles to himself.

He quickly looks up the address in the Appendix and gets the cross-reference, G-23, page 143.

"Good not too far, I should be able to make the appointment and get lunch before my meeting with Bobbi," he mumbles.

On the way over to his newest opportunity, he starts to wonder what Bobbi is scheming. After yesterday's drilling he knows she will be tasking him with something. It seems as though she is constantly trying to get him to do new activities, which usually means qualifying, with more paperwork, some activity in some way, shape, or form. She just doesn't get it! If she would leave him alone maybe he could sell something. But no, she has to always be reviewing him and making sure that he is working. You would think that after all these years that he would have earned the right to more respect than that. In all fairness maybe it wasntt all her fault. That telemarketing program a couple of months ago was a Corporate initiative. And of course it went nowhere fast. "Who has the time to waste on the phone when people need to see you?" he sulks.

"Let's see, right on Euclid and then it should be just a couple more blocks past the old stadium."

His eye catches the old banners of the different championships when his phone rings.

"Joe," he states.

Its Bills and he is as smooth as ever, "Hey Joe, how's Acme's best salesman doing today?"

"OK Bills, but how in the world did you get this number?" Joe challenges Bills.

"I always copy down the number of all incoming

calls if I don't recognize them. I guess you must have called me from this number at some point. I just add the number in my contact software, so that I don't forget it."

"Listen, Bills DO NOT give this number to anyone, uh, OK?" There's a little challenge in this response, but Bills ignores it. Joe continues in a softer tone.

"I had over a three hundred dollar cell bill and I couldn't expense but a small bit," Joe fudges. "So, I got this new number because I just don't have YOUR money to spend on phone calls."

"Come on Joe, I know you have tons of money. If I had your money I'd burn mine," Bills jokes and continues, "I'll keep it a secret, just between us."

"Thanks," Joe concedes, but he's not really sure if Bills will hold this secret close to his vest or carelessly distribute it to any one of their team members when a so-called emergency comes up.

"What did you call me for anyway?"

"Oh, thanks I almost forgot. I have that demo tomorrow with Care Free Leisure and I was hoping that you could give me a little insight into some of the newest options on the 752F."

Joe softens his protective armor a little and appreciates being viewed as an expert and responds, "Bills, I would love to help you. You know I'm the one who coordinated the district launch of the model before this one. It was the 750F. In any case, the 752F copies at 52 pages a minute and it can be configured with four paper supplies that hold a total of 2,150 sheets. Obviously the "F" stands for finisher and I think it now can staple 65 pages...."

Joe is speaking quickly and Bills has to wait until after the specs and prices are thrown at him to ask Joe about the connectivity issues.

"Uh, Joe that's great. Uh, do you know if it comes with the ability to connect using the old Linux J178 NIC (NIC stands for network interface card - this is the card that allows the copier to become a printer on the customer's network)?"

But before Bills can continue with the second half of his train of thought, Joe interrupts again with the specs on the newest NIC. At the end of this barrage of information, Joe confidently states that there is less margin on the cards, so that it really is not worth your time and effort to connect the copiers. "And besides, it just lengthens the sales cycle."

"Yeah, I know it may add some delay in a decision, but I also will be in a better position to help my customer's real problem - their flat productivity," Bills defends.

Bills pushes forward, "Have you ever used either NIC devices to run a lot of one page jobs to the 750F or 752F? What I really want to know is the file formats and the job processing times because Leisure just threw me a curve today when I was following up on my email." Bills always sends an agenda of the demonstration out to all participants the day before their visit to the office. He was following up on that email when Leisure asked if his copier could be connected to their network.

He could have easily and quickly responded that the Acme's open architecture could be adapted to virtually any network and ended it right there and then, but he didn't. He asked them why they changed their minds from a few days ago. And the information flowed for the next twenty minutes with Bills not taking many notes, but listening and jotting down what he perceived as their real issues and then questioning and clarifying his assumptions. Bills didn't think of it as a sales call, but rather an education in how his customer is really doing things and where they want to go.

Now Bills has a dilemma. When he first talked to the customer they were only going to use this new unit for their current workflow, which meant that it was all going to be walk up copying. Now they have described to him a situation that is completely different. He is sure that he could slam a copier in there with little effort, but would it help them as they transition to a more customer-oriented marketing approach? You see Care Free now wants each piece of marketing material to have their customer's name on it. Furthermore, they would really like it if each piece could be customized with different pictures on the front page based on the customer's buying habits. A customer that had purchased, let's say, swimming pool supplies from Care Free Leisure in the past will have pictures of patio furniture whereas a customer that has purchased wind chimes or other lawn decorations will have the appropriate images on their mail pieces.

Bills knows that he could simply print some samples for the customer and have them available for the demonstration, but he would really like to show them how it will actually work. The larger new files may take too long to start printing or the different pictures may slow the process too much and cause delays. There are just too many problems that could go wrong. He needs to test their applications first, but what does he do about the demo tomorrow?

Joe shows some insight by commenting; " If they don't really know what they need then you can lead them by using baby steps and not giant leaps. Talk first about the migration into technology not the drowning in bits and bytes." Joe eventually falls short again and stumbles by adding, "This way you can sell them a machine today and another six months from now."

"I'm sorry what was that?" Bills says.

Joe starts again, "That way you can..."

Bills interrupts him this time and says, "Not that part, the first thing you said."

"Oh, I said, 'you can lead them using baby steps not giant leaps."

Bills is quietly thinking as Joe continues, "Look Bills, just sell this unit tomorrow and then come back in a couple of months and replace it with another unit later. You get two sales at one account," Joe boasts.

Surprisingly Bills likes the idea, but not Joe's entire version. "That's not a bad idea Joe. I'll have to ensure that the customer is aware of what I'm doing and the reasons behind it."

"Thanks for the help, Joe, I've got to run. See you back at the office," Bills states and the line is disconnected.

Joe is happy that his idea helped, but he is not sure that Bills understood because he would not have included the customer in any such discussions. Joe feels like the sales process is his and his alone. You should never discuss with your customers the strategies and intentions. If you do that, you show your hand and are left with nothing to leverage.

Joe drives up to the gate of the Army National Guard base and waits behind five other vehicles. When Joe's car has inched to the front of the line a sentry, dressed in camies marches over. The M-16 weapon is slung over one shoulder and shines with a menacing gleam.

"Sir, may I see your identification, please?" The sentry almost barks.

Joe is a little intimidated and fishes through his wallet for his driver's license. Joe tries to make some small talk, "You ever shoot anyone with that thing?"

"Not today sir. I've noticed you do not have a base decal, so may I have your car's registration please?"

Undaunted by the guard's obvious strict military attitude, Joe continues, " How many rounds can that thing shoot a minute?"

"Sir, that's classified information and I'd have to shoot you if I told you." The guard replies with the slightest of smirks that Joe doesn't catch because the sentry is standing straight and Joe has not bothered to lean out his window.

Joe hands over the requested information and stays quiet.

The guard reviews the documents and continues, "Sir, please state your business and your contact information."

Joe fumbles for a moment before regaining his composure, "Uh, ...I'm uh, here to see a person by the name of, uh, Burnsides, I think. I believe he's in some secretary's office."

"Do you have an appointment, sir?" The guard asks as he towers over the driver's door.

"Well, uh, no, but they called me today and left me a message, so I thought I'd come out and see if I could help them."

"Yes sir, but I cannot let you through without an appointment. Please circle to your right and proceed to that one story building. Inside is the Pass Office where you can call the Major to arrange an escort."

"Will it take long?" Joe's frustration is starting to show.

"Sir, we're still on a high state of security because of the recent events, so you will need to go to the Pass Office to gain entry."

Joe's response is a little forceful, "Look buddy, I'm one of the good guys! I've been on this base before!

Can't you just call the Major?"

"I do not know the Major's where-abouts or his schedule, so I cannot comment on that. Please bear to the right, sir."

Joe, a little more than annoyed snaps, "I don't have time to waste on finding this person, so I'll just call later," Joe sarcastically includes, "Thanks for all of your help."

He's diverted to the exit lane and drives towards the 202 expressway. "They call and then I can't see 'em," he fumes. He jams his foot on the accelerator as he swerves from the merge lane into traffic.

Joe thinks that with any luck he should be by the office at 11:30. Maybe he'll see if Bobbi can move his P&R from three to an earlier slot. He'll swing by the office and see if anyone is there and check his email.

Traffic was light, so it's only 11:20 by the time he parks and walks through the reception area. No one is at the front desk and he wonders if Louise is sick today or if she has finally come to her senses and found a job somewhere else. As he passes the two overstuffed lounge chairs and turns to walk down the hallway, Louise appears from the copy room with a stack of documents. She cradles them in both arms and has her left hand clamped on her right elbow. Joe's not sure if that many sheets of paper is that heavy for her or if she is being cautious not to drop them.

"Hi, Louise, got a match?" Joe chuckles.

"Very funny Joseph. I'm just going to my desk, don't bother to ask if I need a hand or anything," she taunts. "I'm Wonder Woman. I can do three things at once and lift two reams of paper."

Joe continues down the corridor and is quickly in the bullpen. Joe has never counted them, but there must be at least twenty-five cubicles. At one time they all had a salesperson that called it home. That was when things were good and business was great. Today, more than half are used for storage or just vacant waiting for their next owner to hang family pictures and award plaques.

His home sweet home is on the row furthest from the entrance and a straight shot to Bobbi's office.

He has been toying with the idea of moving to one of the other cubicles closer to the door, but he has been in this one for so long, it would take forever to move and re-situate himself. He doesn't think that he has the time. It would be nice to move out of direct line of sight though, especially after comments like the one Bobbi zinged at him yesterday about being late. He thinks he'll be more invisible if he moves twenty feet further away.

Today, Joe gingerly places his briefcase on his chair because yesterday's spill is still fresh. He does a quick walk through the bullpen to see who's there. He meanders up the aisles glancing in each cubicle to see who would like to go to lunch. Toward the front of the bullpen he spots Tom Nowell, a system support engineer, working on his computer with his back to him.

Joe stops and dangles his arm over the corner of the gray partition and says, "Hey Tom, what's going on?"

Tom turns around and smiles at Joe before he raises his finger to his mouth in the universal shhh gesture. Joe immediately sees that the conference button is lit on Tom's phone, so he silently mimics a young boy shoveling cereal in his mouth.

Of course Tom knows what Joe is miming and nods his heads, but gives him three high fives to indicate that he'll be on the call for fifteen more minutes. Joe nods and the silent communication to leave for lunch in fifteen minutes is concluded.

Joe then decides to see if Bobbi is in her office. He

retraces his original route that he used, but he continues just a bit further to Bobbi's office and peeks his head in her open door.

"Nuts," Joe mutters. Bobbi is not in her office and Joe decides to ask Louise if she has seen her or if she knows where she is. Again, Joe walks by his briefcase and his desk to the front entrance. Louise is on the phone with what sounds like an upset customer.

He waits patiently while she calms the customer and tries to find the correct person to send them to. Louise puts the customer on hold and immediately dials another number and talks to Jack in the supply chain. After a short conversation she tells Jack the details of the customer's issue and then connects the two parties, but before she hangs up, Louise pleasantly introduces this customer to Jack and reminds both of them if she can be assistance just to call her back.

Joe nudges closer to the desk as she hangs up and says, "Hey Louise, have you seen Bobbi today?"

"Yeah, Joe she was in her office just a couple of minutes ago. I had forwarded a call in there."

"Well, she's not there now. I'll keep looking around for her, but if you talk to her, please tell her I'm looking for her, OK?" Joe throws these words over his shoulder as he turns and walks back to his desk.

He is just retrieving his first voice message when Tom comes up. Joe listens to half the message about a promotion when he pushes the number seven to save the message. He'll get the other messages when he gets back from lunch. "Hey Tom, where do you want to go today?"

"I don't care Joe, just somewhere fast. I'm way behind the eight ball this afternoon and I need to get back. You want to just grab a burger at MacLand?" Tom asks.

"Yeah, we can do that. Let me just hit the 'head'

first, OK?" Joe asks.

A couple of seconds later, Joe is washing his hands at one of the two sinks and leaning forward a bit to check out his appearance when he hears a unfamiliar voice from the door ask, "Hey Joe." It's a deep hollow voice and he has no idea who it is.

"Yeah," Joe yells.

All at once the bathroom is completely dark. Someone has turned out the lights. "Hey knock it off. Turn the lights on," Joe demands. There's only darkness and silence.

Joe gropes in the blackness for the paper towel dispenser and yanks a sheet free to dry his hands. He tries again to get the phantom to turn on the lights, "Hey, come on I'm blind as a bat in here." Still no light.

"So help me if I catch you, you'll know IT!" Joe yells.

There's snickering from the hallway, but Joe can't run to the door for fear of tripping on the trash can or worse, running into the partition. Joe has to settle for shuffling his feet forward while extending his arms. He feels the wall and moves to his left until he is grasping the corner. Once around the corner there is just the slightest amount of light coming through the bottom grille of the exit door. But there is enough so that Joe can now navigate easily and he opens the door.

A quick look up and down the hallway reveals nothing of the culprit or culprits that did this little prank. "I wonder who did that." Joe is thankful that he was only washing his hands.

After getting their meals they find an all-in-one table and chair unit. They swivel into their seats and begin discussing what's going on at the office, and the different accounts they are working on. Of course, Joe is bragging about what a "sweet" call he had yesterday at

Carroll's Food and Beverage Wholesalers. He's describing their beautiful building and the huge cherry conference table.

Tom is half listening to Joe and wondering what types of computer systems they are running. There would obviously be a mainframe or a mini for inventory. That would be at the headquarters, Tom concludes to himself. Tom is a very knowledgeable system sales engineer with more certifications on his cubicle walls than Joe has awards. A few years back he decided to stay in the industry because of the changes.

Today he views himself, as an integral part of the sales cycle, not just a "fixer upper." Most of the sales people come to him prior to their calls or at least prior to their proposals to ensure that the Acme solution they are recommending is going to work. He still remembers the fiasco from those fax machines that Joe sold at the beginning of the year. The echoing words from Joe were, "Sure, no problem, our SSE's are the best. They can get anything to work." Well this one is still biting them in the ass and they need to do something about it.

Tom opens with, "Hey a Joe, did you get my email about Wednesday's strategy and training sessions this next quarter?"

"Sorry Tom, I must have missed that one. What are these strategy sessions about? You going to teach me how to sell?" Joe replies.

Tom's ego is chipped a little at the last remark, but he lets it slide and continues, "Joe , you're too old to teach anything to. The strategy and training sessions are on the technology side. I can help you uncover bigger, better, and more profitable opportunities. They're only for an hour, every Wednesday from four to five." Before Joe can comment Tom adds, "You know all the fax machines you sold to that company downtown in the first quarter, well we're still working with them. The customer, uh, said that, uh, they wish they had gone with multifunction devices instead. You know they are mostly printing and the fax machines aren't good for that environment. It's taking a lot of effort even today. They call all the time for support and I just don't have the bandwidth to help them."

Joe replies, "The customer bought the fax machines because there was a special pricing promotion and they said they could not afford anything else. And by the way if they need new equipment, I'll swing by sometime and talk to 'em."

"Joe, I'm not talking about upgrading them or selling them new equipment. We need to have them understand that my time isn't free and that they need to pay for support." Tom's concerns are finally voiced. Tom starts dipping his fries in the little mound of ketchup on his hamburger wrapper. His fries are cold.

Joe finishes his last bite of his "slider" and swigs his super-sized root beer soda before commenting. "Tom, I know that the company is making it more difficult for you because of all of the activity tracking forms, but this issue really doesn't affect me. Remember, I put hours into the original proposal for the integration. Maybe what I can do is see if they need a new copier and then I'll pad it with a bunch of hours. The additional hours can be used for the fax machines also. Don't worry; I'll take care of you. Have I ever let you down before?"

That is Tom's exact concern. He is afraid that Joe will do it again and he has very little leverage except to have Bobbi get involved on every sale. Maybe he'll luck out and Joe will come to the training. He's not putting any bets on it though.

As Tom is shaking his head in reply to Joe's question, he silently thinks that Joe just doesn't get it.

Back at the office, Bobbi is at her desk when Joe finds her.

"Hey Bobbi, I'm glad I found you." Joe smiles warmly as he peeks his head around the corner of her office. "I was trying to find you before lunch, but it just wasn't meant to be. I uh was hoping that we could move the plan and review session to maybe, uh, now."

Bobbi, stops writing in the margin of a report and puts down her pen. She has a busy afternoon, but waits patiently for Joe to complete his request and then replies, "Joe, if you can get Melissa to change her slot with you, I don't have any problem with it."

"Thanks Bobbi, I'll go talk with her now," Joe states as he heads towards Melissa's desk.

Melissa isn't there, so Joe decides to finish his emails and voice mails that he just couldn't get to before lunch. First, he has to connect his IBM ThinkPad to the company's snail mail system. Boy, when is someone going to upgrade these antiquated processes? If they could just increase the speed of the network he is sure he would be able to answer all his emails. It is just too slow to be a benefit. He longs for the days of memos on pure white sheets of paper. Now that's the way business got done. You could grab all your information from one "in-basket" and take it with you. No matter where you were you could read it. You didn't have to be connected to some digital umbilical cord. Today, it's just too easy for people to email you and task you with doing their jobs. The only people that use email are the ones that don't want to do their jobs or want to cover their backsides.

Once again, his screen is covered in red and he immediately looks at the senders.

It doesn't take a rocket scientist to figure out what Bishop's email will be about. He doesn't open it and scrolls down further. Joe doesn't realize yet that Bobbi has offered to take over his membership on the committee. He reviews the subject lines of the next four messages before he finds one from marketing about a new sales promotion and contest. He double clicks on it. After reviewing the "YEAR END BLOW OUT" contest rules and qualifications, he decides that he may have a chance to make a little extra money. It seems that Acme is determined to sell the remainder of the old analog copiers at steep discounts. The contest states that all salespeople are invited to participate and that the top three will win a ski trip to a luxurious mystery destination, plus $500 spending money.

"This is right up my alley," Joe mutters.

None of the other five emails generate enough interest to be opened. The sea of red grows a bit larger.

Joe's spirits are flying as he thinks of steep slopes covered in pure white snow. He's looking in his Rolodex for Melissa's cell number when his phone rings, "Joe."

"Hi, this is Major Burnsides and I was hoping that I could speak with someone about a copier or multifunctional device."

"Yeah, Major this is Joe Sails. I got your message this morning and I went out to your base a couple of hours ago. The knucklehead guard wouldn't let me in," Joe offers as a humorous afterthought.

"Did you tell him you wanted to see me?" the Major's tone is inquisitive.

"Sure and he said I couldn't come in without an appointment or escort. I didn't have time to waste going through all of the specifics, so I was going to call you later. In any case how can I help?" Joe concludes.

The Major isn't sure if Joe is complaining about the regulations or the guard, so he decides to let it drop and get to the business of why he was calling. "We have an old copier that just doesn't seem to be working well.

I'm not sure if we're over using it or if it's just too old. I wanted to talk with someone about maybe getting a new device."

"Major, we have lots of reasons that people get machines from Acme. We believe in putting our customers first and pride ourselves on our work ethic. I'll do everything I can to marry you with the right product. Do you mind if I ask a couple of questions about your workflow?" Joe asks.

"No, go right ahead, but shouldn't we make an appointment, so that you can come out here and see how we do things?" asks the Major.

"Sure we can, but let me just get an idea, so I know what were dealing with." He doesn't pause for an answer and leads right into his first question, "What's the make of your current copier?"

After eight or ten questions, Joe is confident that he has as much information as he needs: monthly volumes, accessories, leasing desires, funding, etc.

"Thank you sir for this information. I think I've got just the right copier for you. Based on what you have just told me I think there's a basis to do business. How about we get together next week, let's say, uh, hum... Thursday at three?" Joe offers.

"When you say copier, does that mean multifunction device?"

Joe replies, "I was thinking of some of our superior analog equipment."

"That's great, but I want you to bring some information on some of your new digital products too. I've been told that they're less expensive and can connect to my network just like my little printers," says the Major.

"Major, I'll bring some literature out on our digital portfolio, but with the prices I'm going to show you, I'll be surprised if you even consider one of the digital boxes.

Most people just use them as expensive copiers. I bet I haven't connected ten in the last year." Joe insists. Joe wants to win the skip trip.

"Ok, Joe I'll hear what you have to say. But, I can't see you this Thursday, we have exercises," says the Major. "I'll call you in two or three weeks to set a fixed date, OK?"

"Thanks again, Major. You won't be disappointed, bye," Joe says.

Just as they are about to hang up the Major remembers, "Hold on, Joe, make sure when you do come out here that you have your car's registration, license and company ID with you. That way I can have a pass waiting for you in the Pass Office at the front gate and since you'll have an appointment, you will not need an escort. Please give me the spelling of your last name."

When the Major is done gathering the information Joe hangs up and proceeds to look yet again for Melissa's number. But before he can find it, he hears her as she approaches his desk.

"Hey, Joe how's life in the fast lane?" she asks.

"Great Melissa, if it were any faster I'd have to get a driver's license. Hey is there any chance that I can switch P&R slots with you?"

"Ah, Joe I can't. I have a 3:30 appointment on the other side of town. And I don't think I'll be able to get there, go over the proposal and get back in time," she explains.

Joe tries another approach, "Heck, you could just drop it off and tell them you'll call and discuss the prices later."

Melissa and Joe have been in the office the longest and she truly likes him although lately he has been "pushing her buttons" quite a lot. It used to be very competitive between her and Joe several years ago.

Many times there would only be a two spot difference in their stack ranking positions. It had always been friendly competition, with them zinging each other about who was the best and talk about "cake" territories. Lately, things have been different. Joe's digs have been a little deeper and closer to the bone, but Melissa understands how frustrated Joe must feel. She just cannot tolerate his intolerance to change. In this business they are always changing and he needs to be a little more adaptive. If you stick to the old ways you will be stuck in one stop too long and everyone else will pass you by.

She thinks that Joe has been running in one place too long and that the competition is passing him by. This last question he just asked is a perfect example. You cannot just drop off pricing and rush sales cycles anymore. Enduring loyalties are a thing of the past and the competition is too fierce. You can never stop selling even after a customer has given you a verbal approval. Today the sales process doesn't end until the unit is delivered. Even at that point you must continue to stay close to your largest customers because they are constantly being bombarded with information from the competition. If you are not proactive and diligent your competition will beat you.

"There isn't a snowball's chance that I'll just drop off pricing. Heck, you're the one that taught me that," Melissa mildly reproaches him.

"Yeah, I know. I was just hoping," Joe concedes.

Melissa excuses herself and goes to her desk to put the finishing touches on her "Forecaster" form for her P&R in fifteen minutes. Joe sits at his desk and thinks of what he should do next. Joe takes this lull to retrieve his voice mail.

This time when he tries to retrieve his messages a metallic voice reminds him that his mailbox is more than

92% full and that he has two new messages and 24 saved messages. He hears this all the time, so he's not too concerned. He listens to them and starts to retrieve his saved messages. He hangs up after the third one and says, "Shoot, I forgot to call service from yesterday."

He pokes at the buttons on his phone, 1 800 A O K-ACME and leaves a message for the service technician, Eddie Coupling. "Eddie, this is Joe. I'm sorry I was real busy yesterday and have just now found a free minute to give you a call. Sorry, I missed you. Please give me a call at your convenience. Thanks, Joe."

He then decides to start getting his paperwork together for his session with Bobbi. He retrieves his "Forecaster" form from his file cabinet at the side of his desk. Joe likes to highlight all the accounts that he is working on in the 30 and 60-day cycles. Bobbi has been after him to submit this electronically for the last three months. She has given him to the end of the month to have it completed. Technically, he has until Friday, the last day of the month to get it done. Since today is Tuesday he'll just correct last months and walk her through it. Joe tells himself that he'll have "Bobbi's version" done by Friday.

"Lets see, I'll mark completed the All Square order and add the Carroll's to my 60-day section. Hmm, what else have I been working on," Joe muses. He remembers several other customers that he has talked to earlier in the month and adds those names to the "60 days or more" section. Just as he is about to walk to the nearest copier to make Bobbi's set, he remembers to add the Army National Guard as a strong prospect because of the great pricing and promotion. This causes him to stop and think about how many of his current sales' cycles that he'll be able to change to the analog boxes.

A few seconds later he has totaled all of his

suspects and prospects. The total is fourteen potential customers, with three that have a chance of closing this next month. If he can get all three, he'll have made his quota for the first time in a long time. The remainder of the group is in various stages of their sales' cycle. He has got to find a way to move the Carroll's Food and Beverage Wholesalers' cycle ahead. Maybe he could go back to them with this special analog copier pricing, but it's going to be difficult because of his little speech on digital.

Joe decides to leave everything the way it was because he just found out about the promotion today and no one would expect him to update his "Forecaster" that quickly.

He walks over to the copier and makes a copy of the document for Bobbi and waits as the set is stapled. He picks up his document and continues walking to the demonstration room. After Bills comments yesterday, his curiosity is peaked and he wants to make sure what equipment is still in there. Joe has no scheduled customer demos, but he may want to ask Bobbi about the status in his P&R. His rationale is you can't sell equipment without demonstration units. So, the condition of the demonstration room is extremely important.

If Joe were to think about this, he would initially say that he was being proactive, but the fact of the matter is that Joe is looking for excuses of why he hasn't been successful. Times are changing, but Joe hasn't faced the music that he must change. As though his coach were whispering in his ear he can still hear, 'Great players don't have one good game, great players have great careers.'

As he is walking out of the showroom's double wooden doors, he notices that the time has slipped by him and that it is close to three o'clock.

He pops his head into the break room to see if there is any coffee, none. Melissa is just opening Bobbi's door when Joe walks up.

"Hey, Melissa you don't look any worse for wear. You must've forecasted a lot," Joe says in greeting her.

"Joe, you know the routine. Just give your name, rank and serial number and you'll be done in no time," she banters back. In all actuality, she and Bobbi have been having some very constructive P&Rs. They seem to be strategizing more and more about accounts and relationship building.

Joe walks to Bobbi's desk and hands her a copy of his "Forecaster." He then goes back to the door and silently closes it. He can't remember the exact date that he started to dread these sessions, but lately he would rather be stuck in a cage with a lion then go through all of this snooping.

"Joe, let's quickly go through the results for this month and next month's forecast. We have to discuss several other important matters," she informs him.

Great, she's going to force him to be Bishop's little puppet. "No problem," Joe lies.

The numbers are again low, but Joe reassures her that he will close these three customers that are leaning his way and he'll be on track again. Bobbi has heard it before and lets Joe finish his monologue.

"Joe, it is my turn, and I'm asking you not to interrupt until I'm finished, OK?"

"Sure Bobbi."

"Joe, you have historically been a great producer, but since I've been here you have only made your monthly quota twice in the last eleven months." Joe begins to object when Bobbi holds up one hand as if she is stopping traffic and says, "You had your say now it's

MY turn." Joe backs down immediately. He knows when not to tangle with her, and this is one of those times.

Bobbi's voice is still full of authority, "Joe, I've let you lose perspective. You are no longer the lead dog, yet you act like it. Remember this, people will treat you the way you treat them." She pauses for effect. "And it starts right now. From now on you will no longer interrupt me. Is that clear?"

"Sure Bobbi."

She's motionless. She looks directly at Joe and says nothing and then continues. "Now I believe the changes that Acme is going through and the changes in our industry, are making it difficult for you to achieve the same results that you are use to. And that has caused some fundamental shifts in your behavior. Remember that everyone is a customer. It is just a matter of whether they are an internal customer or external customer. So we are going to immediately implement two ideas that will positively affect business. The first idea is a shared calendar."

"At our next P&R we'll talk more about the essence of customer care, but for now I need you to get organized with a digital calendar that I can review." Bobbi turns her computer almost 180 degrees, so that Joe can see her screen and continues in a tone closer to normal.

"Joe, I need you closing deals. I can't have you not being productive. So, you and I will be sharing this calendar for the next couple of months. When I add something from my computer it will show up on the calendar in green and when you add something it will show up on my screen in green."

"You have to download from the server the newest calendar and update it daily."

"Did you say daily?" Joe asks incredulously.

"That's correct Joe."

"Bobbi that's ridiculous. I'm not going to do it!"

"Joe, I only have a couple of options and the other one would mean I would have to put you on corrective action," she explains. She waits with hands folded.

Joe can't believe this. This is crazy. But he has no alternative. "So you want all of my sales calls on this?" Joe asks.

"No, Joe I want all of your activities from sales calls to administrative work to customer research. Every day should have a minimum of fifteen to twenty activities."

Joe is not sure what to say or do. He knows that Bobbi has been patient with him and could have already written him up for poor performance, so he reluctantly just accepts this new intrusion and replies, "Bobbi, I'll have this downloaded by the end of the week."

"Joe, I have yet to mention just a couple of other items. Like I said, you will need to view this calendar and update it every day either remotely or from the office. I will then be able to view when and what changes you have made." She appeases him by saying, "Joe, I'm trying to make you more productive by ensuring that you have set job-related activities every day and that you don't get too distracted."

"Every night I'll be reviewing this. If I have any questions I will call you to discuss them. I will be tasking you with problem accounts and I want you to stay as close to the schedule as possible. If I feel that you are not being honest or fully committed, I will immediately start corrective action. Is this clear?"

Joe slowly nods.

"One final thing Joe. I am convinced of your capabilities and believe that the steps we are taking today and in the future will ensure your long-term employment with Acme." Bobbi sits relaxed with her hands still folded staring directly at Joe waiting for his reply.

Since he can't think of any arguments. Joe simply stands up and tells Bobbi he'll have this downloaded by Friday.

"Joe, please sit," Bobbi motions to his recently vacated chair and waits.

After he is seated, "Yeah?"

Bobbi can see the disappointment and frustration, but she can't relinquish for Joe's sake. "Joe, you will download that immediately and add the task of submitting your 'Forecaster' to me digitally. If you are serious about getting it done you should be able to email me our updated calendar before the end of the day. I also want to see your schedule for tomorrow."

"I expect the rest of your week's activities in the update by close of business tomorrow. Any questions on the calendar, Joe?"

"Great, our second initiative is to get me in the field more to understand what our customers issues are." Bobbi now tries to pacify Joe and bolster his ego. "Joe, I can learn a lot from you which will help develop better customer programs. I need to spend more time in front of our customers. All I want to do is work with you on that new account we were talking about. Let's see..." She looks at the copies that Joe placed on her desk to find the name, Carroll's Food and Beverage Wholesaler.

"Bobbi, can I say one thing?" Joe's question is meek.

"Sure, Joe shoot."

Joe thinks shoot is a very appropriate word. He feels as though he is on the receiving end of a firing squad. "Bobbi, look I want your help and the truth be known I can use it, but to get into my accounts may not be the best thing to do. I need you to get me equipment and trial units. I need better lease rates and longer warranty periods."

Last night when Bobbi was trying to strategize on how she was going to approach these changes, she wanted Joe to admit that his numbers were not good. And that he should get refocused. Joe's initial comment was exactly what she felt Joe needed. He, of course, put a twist on it, though. She cannot allow him to walk away from working on an account with her because this is not about activity management. It is all about the customer. Joe is HER customer and she refuses to let him fail without her dedicated efforts.

"Joe, I, uh, appreciate the fact that you have so much concern for your customers, but trust me I've been on a few sales calls in my career and will not lose any business for you." Again she pauses and challenges Joe with a stare that penetrates his multiple layers of defense.

"I'm not sure if you've heard yet, but I'm now going to be on the supply chain committee. You are no longer obligated. Any other questions? Great, I'll review your calendar at 5:00." This is Bobbi's not so subtle way of reminding Joe not to blow off the first part of their conversation.

"Thanks Joe."

With that Joe exits without saying a word and begrudgingly starts to work on Bobbi's calendar. He wonders if there's life after Acme.

This was the first step in changing Joe's core behaviors. She has to show Joe what he's doing wrong and he has to admit to himself that he needs help. He has taken a partial first step. She can't just dictate what he is doing is wrong because he'll just push back. Joe has to see his mistakes; take ownership; feel the pain and want to change. Then he will be open to better core behaviors. The theory is he will then internalize them and they will become his own. The key to this transformation is not to stop short. This will be a long process, and Bobbi realizes that if she isn't in it for the long haul she will fail.

Bobbi has to ensure that Joe sees the right way of doing things and bring him back to an even keel.

But how is she going to do that?

Chapter 3

trap

The red high glossed Honda Civic swerves in his lane about four car lengths ahead. "Look at that idiot!" Joe yells, "What a moron!" It has been more than a week since his P&R with Bobbi and he still has a burn about it. He is a professional salesperson with over ten years selling. Doesn't seniority or experience count for anything around this place? Now he is being treated like a neophyte salesperson. If he wanted to start over, he would have gone to a bigger and better company long ago. He cut his teeth on copiers and now they're treating him like a baby. It's 10:00 o'clock on Friday morning and Joe is heading to his third appointment

After Tuesday's meeting with Bobbi, Joe had to work until 5:30 getting his calendar and "Forecaster" completed. Bobbi had thanked him before he left, but it was little consolation. He was stuck in traffic for an hour and half. If he could have left at 5:00, he would have been home at 6:00.

He has talked more to Bobbi in the last three days than he has in the last three months. The only saving grace is that maybe she'll tire of all of this handholding and get back to the way it was. Joe believes he still has what it takes to be a successful salesperson in this business, the gift of gab. Time is on his side. He also has to be honest with himself. It's nice that Bobbi's ideas are being handled discretely and that everyone on the team is not aware of his humiliation. That speaks well of Bobbi because she could have lightened her load by allowing Louise to handle the calendars.

The downside to all of this is that he feels as though he is running so fast that he isn't really selling. All of Bobbi's activities on his calendar seem to be housekeeping chores that don't do anything for his monthly sales quota. If she thinks that he'll be able to keep this up and still make his numbers, she's crazy. "You can't get blood out of a turnip," he quips to himself. Although, it was nice to finally get that billing issue resolved for OPQC. In retrospect it really wasn't a complicated issue. At first, Jimmy Panteous was a little upset at Joe for not showing up for over a week, but after the problems were fixed he seemed genuinely pleased. Joe just wished he could have found the time earlier to help him.

After this appointment, he is supposed to have lunch with Bobbi to go over the strategy for the Carroll's account. Joe is still trying to figure a way out of letting Bobbi in.

Joe feels upbeat today and he's not really sure why. Maybe it's because today is Friday or maybe it's because tonight his high school's football team has their season opener. Of course Joe is an avid fan and hopes that they will win and go to Regionals, but the prospects look gloomy to say the least. Tonight's opponents, the Falcons, finished almost in the basement last year, one win less than his team, the Cougars. Joe thinks that it should be a close game, but the fact that his Cougars don't have a stronger running game, will probably mean that they will lose. Going to the games is Joe's Friday ritual and he will stay by his team in the good and bad times. He's just more vocal in the bad times.

He finally arrives at his next appointment and makes a mental note to get their web address. Bobbi wants all web addresses for every prospect and customer. This is not only a requirement of Joe, but of all of her salespeople. Information is the key to winning business and customers' Websites are the doors to that information.

After a brief twenty minutes in the customer's offices, Joe is walking back to the front desk with the customer.

"Thanks again for your time today," Joe comments as they round the corner towards the reception area.

"Joe, I wish I could have had more time to answer your questions. Next week when you come back, I'll make sure that the copier manager is here," the gentleman replies.

"Thanks. Maybe I should have suggested that on the phone a couple of days ago. It really doesn't matter though; it was nice to meet you and to get a quick look around. Oh, one other thing, I didn't see a web address for your company on your card. Do you have an Internet site that I could go to? I would really like to be able to understand your company better," Joe adds.

"We have a Website if that's what you mean."

Several minutes later, Joe is back in his car driving to the office. If traffic is light he should be at least twenty-five minutes early for his working lunch with Bobbi. Maybe I'll call her and see if I can pick up something to eat at The Deli on the way over.

"Hey Bobbi, I'm on my way in. Are we going to have a working lunch in the conference room or are we going out?

"Joe, I was going to order us some subs from Express Delivery, but if you want to stop at The Deli I would rather have a tuna Caesar salad. Oh yeah, add a slice of their bread of the day, OK?" Bobbi asks.

"Sure Bobbi."

"I'll get it straight with you when you get in here," she replies. Which means she'll pay him for her salad when he sees her.

Joe hurries across the busy parking lot. The new pharmacy in the front out parcel has increased the traffic in the parking lot quite a bit. It used to be that you could park only a space or two away from The Deli at 12:30 in the afternoon. Now, Joe is all the way down the crowded aisle of cars and it's not even 11:30. "For cryin' out loud," Joe complains and shakes his head, "Lunch hour doesn't start for another 30 minutes."

He's sixth in line where he used to be first. The only saving grace is that there are still customers piling in after him and he is at least ahead of them. He orders the ham and cheese and Bobbi's lunch to go. The counter help asks, "Would you mind standing over there while your food is being prepared?" And points towards the rack of assorted chips, in the corner. On his way to the waiting area he picks up the morning sports page and rustles the pages until he finds the article on tonight's game. It will be an early kick off at 7:00. So he'll have to make sure that he remembers to leave his house at 6:15.

His old coach is still predicting a great year with his run and gun strategy. "... quickness will be on our side, so we'll be doing a lot of roll outs and short passes. Once the defense adjusts and starts to come up too fast to cover, we'll have the long ball deep." If nothing else y'Ol Blood and Guts can make it sound easy.

"Thirty-six"

"Yeah, right here, Dan," Joe responds, and reaches for the brown bag. "Did you put the mustard on the side and include the slice of today's bread?"

Since this is Joe's favorite lunch spot, most of the help knows him and Dan Cook is no exception. "Joe have I ever messed up your order?"

Joe peers inside the bag and says, "No, but there is always a first time."

"Thanks ... Joe," says Dan in a tone that Joe is not sure if it is sarcastic or not.

Within minutes Joe is placing his briefcase by his desk and walking to Bobbi's office. The brown bag in just a normal nondescript wrinkled bag, but the aroma is mouth watering. Even before he pops into Bobbi's office she yells, "That smells great, what did you get?"

"I got my favorite, ham 'n cheese."

Joe's halfway in her office when she replies," I still need fifteen minutes. Leave the bag and send me your calendar before we start, OK?"

"Hey Bobbi, I thought we were going to talk about Carroll's. I don't have my calendar updated."

"I know we're scheduled to talk about Carroll's, but I have another idea. And besides it will only take five minutes to update it from yesterday."

Joe leaves her office madder than he has been in the last couple of days. She is making my life miserable he decides. I even brought her lunch and she asks for more. "What a...," Joe thinks under his breath.

At his desk, he boots his computer and within no time at all he's connected and updating yesterday's and today's activities. As he types he realizes that his days have been fuller than he thought. His conclusion is that he has been very busy. His anger subsides as he takes note of his calendar. "Not a bad week's work," he says in review. He sends the reports and copies his own set.

Now it's Bobbi's turn to poke her head around the corner. "You ready, amigo?" she asks.

Joe follows her into the office. The red-hot anger that he had felt just moments ago is barely just a warm memory.

Bobbi opens the bag and retrieves her lunch and forces the prongs of the plastic fork through its wrapper. That done she opens the salad container and begins to eat. Joe has decided to claim a corner of her desk as his lunch table. As he pulls his sandwich from the bag some napkins float to the floor. Joe bends over and hands a couple to Bobbi.

"Anks." Is her reply because her mouth is full as she grabs a napkin and covers her mouth. She finishes her first bite and dabs her mouth before she moves the napkin to her lap. "This is wonderful. You know you can always count on them for great food every time. They are consistent."

They munch in silence for a few more minutes both looking at Joe's calendar and coming away with completely different thoughts about it. Joe believes that he has been very busy and productive while Bobbi sees Joe's numerous activities are a good start, but far from the positive productivity that she needs.

She believes that Joe is still procrastinating the difficult parts of his job. He is pushing too many issues to the end of the day. This, she sees as a barrier that Joe must tear down. It is like having a cloud over your head and never getting any relief until the ride home. Furthermore, she actually believes that it affects his sales because when someone is dreading to do something they are not as "up" and positive during their other sales activities. The first thing a salesperson needs to do is exude confidence and have a positive personality. No matter what you are selling people still buy from people.

If your personality is such that your customers are uncomfortable or uneasy, then it is a much harder sell even if you're selling water in the desert.

The other factor in the equation is Joe's lack of success. Failure can certainly turn even the most competent salesperson into an order grabbing pit bull. They'll start to see every sale as do or die. And that can be too much for most customers. There is a difference between being inoffensively aggressive and too pushy. A professional will lead a customer with determination and logic. A desperate salesperson will annoy and distance himself from customers by almost demanding that they buy from him or her. Bobbi is not sure where Joe's current state lies, but she knows that she must work on his self-image first.

Bobbi needs to pull Joe's positive self-image back into his actions. He may be cocky on the outside, but he is actually self-defeating. His mind has justified his failures and caused his activities to change. His days do not reflect a customer-focused salesperson. One could describe his days as more of a hectic series of isolated events than a choreographed process. He is reacting and not strategizing. He's groping for opportunities where none exist. She has to draw out his successful self-image. Like most salespeople, Joe believes in himself and knows he's qualified. He has years of experience to prove it, yet deep down he knows something is different because his numbers do not reflect his image. After a while even the cockiest, most self-absorbed salesperson realizes that he or she is always trailing the pack. This leads to building shells and layers of issues to protect themselves. Bobbi then realizes that Joe's tantrums are his excuses for not selling. It is Joe's way of pushing blame to others.

Bobbi must get Joe to act like a winner, but before he acts he must think like he is going to be successful.

She could easily tell him, "You're a great asset, Joe." But she is concerned with building him up when she may actually have to release him if he doesn't change. Furthermore, a quick complement from her will not pull Joe forward.

The second part of the self-image problem is that once Bobbi gets Joe to see himself as a success again she must then get him to mirror that image to all of his customers. She wants Joe to treat everyone with careful attention and consideration. Sometimes opportunity has a funny way of knocking. Bobbi believes that successful people make the time to do their job right.

"Why do you need to follow that order?" she says to herself in a challenge. "More good would come from customer and peer comments than from my mouth."

"Hey Joe, great week, so far. I've got a couple of good ideas that I hope you don't mind discussing."

Joe's sarcasm is as thick as his accent, "Sure, El Capitano. Your wish is my command."

Bobbi settles into her logic and lets Joe's sarcastic remarks land with a thud. "Joe, it looks like you've been doing some of the dirty housekeeping chores that all of us hate."

"I see you resolved the billing issues at OPQC. What happened there?"

They talk for several minutes about that account before they move on to the core of Bobbi's concern. "I want you to schedule the customer issue appointments first thing in the mornings if you can."

"What do you mean?" Joe's temperature is on the rise.

"Joe, I would rather you do the crap jobs first thing in the morning. That way your schedule will be free the rest of the day for selling opportunities." She explains further, "We all like to sell Joe, and no one likes to do the clean up. I just want you to schedule the customer issue appointments as early as possible, OK?"

"Bobbi, don't you think you're going a little too far with this scheduling stuff? I mean come on," he throws his hands up in an expression of exhaustion and frustration. He leans back in his chair and wearily says, "I've done pretty good this week."

"I know Joe, but you missed some appointments and pushed them back a couple of days. If they were closing calls, you would never have missed them."

Changing gears she says, "Joe, I see here that a week from Wednesday looks wide open. How about if you travel with Bill for a blitz day? I still want to see you in action at Carroll's, but I was hoping that you two could travel a couple of times in the next few weeks. I would then like to do some traveling with you, too."

There is no indication from Joe whether he wants to do it or not. He just sticks his hand deeper into his miniature bag of chips and acts like he hasn't heard Bobbi.

"Joe, I want to get out of this office and see some of our customers again. I know I said I wanted to visit Carroll's, but I also have to keep in touch with our strategic customers, to ensure that we have done everything we can to support them." At once, she knows she has stepped on Joe's ego by insinuating that he wasn't able to handle his own customers. So she quickly added, "The fact of the matter is, that I need to help Bishop with the supply chain issues and I was hoping that I could glean some first hand information."

"Uh Bobbi, I don't have a lot scheduled for the later part of next week because I have to be a little flexible to handle all the new appointments that you keep throwing at me."

Bobbi nods with her eyes still on Joe and says,

"Touché. I understand that this isn't easy. It certainly isn't easy for me either, but I believe it is the right thing to do for you. I hope you understand that."

"Let's do a whole day of travel. I'll even treat you to lunch if we make any sales calls in the morning and afternoon." They decide that Bobbi will be traveling with Joe at the end of the month.

As Joe is leaving the office he says, "Thanks Bobbi, I'll let you know if I can firm up these appointments. And like you said, I'll explain that we would like to initiate strategic reviews with them to discuss any issues and/or trends that may be occurring. That was a great idea." Joe's words are sincere.

Bobbi, " Don't break your arm patting yourself on your back." She does not want Joe to walk out of her office feeling dejected or caged.

"I thought it was you that came up with that idea," Joe honestly replies.

"I don't think so...let's just tell everyone it was OUR idea. If it works well, I'll initiate it for all of our major customers. In the meantime, while you're on the phone make sure you ask them to come in for the open house in a couple of weeks." Joe quickly leaves her office before she can task him with anything else.

Bobbi is left in her now empty office hoping that her plan doesn't backfire.

Just as he is getting to his desk, Joe's phone rings. He picks up the phone and says, "Acme Joe here, can I help you?" The phone keeps ringing.

For a half of a second Joe is confused and just looks at the handset.

Ring!

He then pulls the cord and notices that it's not connected to the base.

Ring!

He quickly plugs it in, but he's too late. He only hears a dial tone. When he places his phone back into the cradle his voice mail light is flashing.

He glances around, and yells to anyone in the bullpen, "So help me when I catch you, you'll pay!"

Chapter 4

game

Joe notices that the days are getting shorter as he rushes to make the opening ceremony. It won't be too long before it will be dark on his commute home.

He'll always remember that football is such a unique sport because you start practicing in the August heat with fifteen pounds of equipment. Most schools like his have doubles in the summer, which means you arrive at school at 8:00 and practice all morning until noon for the first session. Then there is a two-hour break for food and lots of liquids. At 2:00, the drills and scrimmages start again. By 5:30 you're drained and you want to drop and sleep.

But the unique part of football is that the players wear all this gear to protect themselves. They have the mandatory protection of helmets, pants, shoulder pads, mouth guards and protection for other places. In addition, some players will also wear visors, rib guards and an assortment of leg and arms pads. At the beginning of the season in the hot weather you can't stand it. Players will be tilting their helmets back and praying that the afternoon session is helmets only, no pads. That means there will be no hitting or tackling.

The coaches will run play after play to make sure that every player on the field knows their position and their role.

One plays football to hit one's opponents, not to stand around in the hot sun tired and delirious from lack of water; listening to a coach talking about what will happen four months from now when your competition may show this formation or do this or that. So while you may want to hit someone, the elements (sun and heat) are working against you. But no one wants to be yanked from the field either. Each player loves the adrenaline that scrimmages and games hold. No matter how hot, being on the field with fifteen pounds of equipment, is better than sitting on the sidelines watching. On the sideline, you feel the heat and the sun in your eyes, but when you are on the field nothing else matters.

Four months later, the weather has changed and you huddle to stay warm when you're not in the game. Players keep their helmets on and even don additional protection to brave the new elements-wind and freezing conditions. Heaters are on the sidelines trying to force pockets of warmth in the surrounding cold. Warmth that will allow muscles not to contract and stop fingers and toes from tingling. Hands are shoved in places that would normally cause stares. Invisible pogo jumping is a common past time. The players on the sidelines try to survive the lull, so that they're ready to hit someone as soon as they are back in the game.

Like the summer, you don't feel the elements when you're on the field and the ball is snapped. Every thought and action is based on all the drills and practices. You know their formation; you know their strengths. Now you execute with determination, power and finesse. Your job is to perform your part, so your game plan is successful. Nothing else matters. You give it your all. If you fail once, you keep trying. Minute-by-minute you fight and scratch to victory. Few victories are easy. Your opponents change their game plan to match their strengths against your weaknesses. There is no time for slacking for even though your team may be winning there is always the possibility for injury. You play every play with fierce determination as much for the team as for self-preservation. There is no letting up!

"Boy, I used to love playing football," Joe mutters to himself as he slides out of his car and heads towards the stadium. It's not even 7:00 and the stadium is half full.

"What was that honey?" Joe's wife, Izzy says. She hasn't used her full name since grade school - Isabelle. Joe has never ventured to call her by her full name and doesn't expect to any time soon. He knows she doesn't like it.

"Oh, nothing. You know how I get when we come to these games. I just love football and every time I come back to a game, I remember everything like it was yesterday. And Izzy I'm not talking that I just remember the wins that we had. I remember the battles and the losses. I can even sometimes taste the dirt and almost feel the grit in my teeth. It was such a big part of my life when I was younger. Sometimes, I wish I could have that passion again. I do miss it."

Izzy, "I know you do Joe. One of the first things that I noticed was your passion and compassion. I know you didn't have a lot of compassion on the field, but off the field you have always been a good person. That's uh, why I hate to see you this way about work Joe. Just give it time and you'll be back on top before you know it."

"Thanks Izzy. I truly do appreciate your support even if I don't tell you all the time."

Joe thinks that maybe he has started to change the

way that he is working. Maybe he isn't doing the fundamentals as well as he used to. Like football drills, sales fundamentals must constantly be repeated and practiced. "Ol' Blood and Guts" would say, "Practice doesn't make you perfect. Perfect practice makes you perfect."

Joe concludes that he has never avoided work, but maybe now he is avoiding the difficult tasks and only doing the least painful part of his job. He continues to try to compare his football days to his current job. Although Joe will not admit it, subconsciously he knows that he has lost some of his passion and this is causing him to accept losing.

They're at the entrance gate and the ticket-taker is one of his old teachers. To Joe she hasn't chnage one bit in the last 14 years. "Hi Ms. Durick," Joe's greeting is playful as he slightly changes his pitch.

"Hello Joseph Sails. I'm glad you could make the opening game."

"I wouldn't miss it for the world. Any word on how we look this year?" Joe asks as he moves toward her. There are lots of people in front and back of him, so his strides are very short, almost like a shuffle.

"Joe, you know I always think that we're going to have a great year. The kids have been practicing very hard."

When Joe is directly in front of her he bends down slightly and whispers, "Come on Ms. Durick, just tell me what "Ol' Blood and Guts" has been saying. I know you teachers just sit in that lounge of yours and gossip all day."

"Mr. Sails, that will be enough from you," she says and slaps his arm. She gives Joe a wink and says, "I think you'll be surprised. They have been working very diligently and their hopes are high."

"Thank you, Ms. Durick. Your words of inspiration are always welcome," Joe gallantly adds.

Joe and Izzy are mildly fighting the crowd with little bumps and contacts as they jostle their way to the aluminum bleachers on the fifty-yard line. Joe has been coming to the Cougars home games every year for the last five years. Although, Joe gets excited and frustrated, he does have fun. He's a very loyal fan and has eternal hope that his team will once again prevail.

The crushed stones from the outside track crinkle under foot as he and Izzy increase their strides toward the steps. Joe is on the third step when he stops to answer. Izzy continues to find a seat in the middle of the bleachers. "Yes sir coach, I'll be here all season cheering our team on."

"Good, but this year I want to hear you or so help me you'll be running laps," 'Ol' Blood and Guts' " sneers.

Not missing a beat Joe replies, "I'm faster now than I've ever been, sir."

"Joe, you were never fast. "Bubble Butt" could beat you in the forty," the coach replied as he turned his head to review the warm-up drills.

Joe smiles at the reference to one of his old teammates and trots up the remaining steps to where his wife is sitting. Taking big breaths he says, "Boy, Izzy I hope they win this one."

Joe watches the rest of the warm-up drills with little comment. Friends that are climbing the steps frequently interrupt him. The remarks are typically just greetings, but occasionally there are short conversations, which always seem to end in laughter. Joe has always been popular and a good friend.

As the teams line the field for the opening kick-off, Joe's conclusion is that this new quarterback may actually have an arm, but the jury is out as to whether the pressure will be too much for him.

Izzy is busy yacking with several of her friends and Joe is engrossed with the game. He sporadically leans over and whispers something to a friend, but he stays focused on the game and yells louder than anyone else in his section. "Come on you guys, concentrate." "Great tackle!" "Good play." Joe has always been a supportive fan. He honestly believes that encouragement is a better motivator than negativism.

After the first half, Joe thinks that his Cougars are doing well even though there is no score. They're moving the ball well and their defense is strong. He thinks that the big "D" has only given up one first down. As far as the run and gun offense, they have done pretty well, but some crucial mistakes and turnovers have cost them. Joe is still not convinced that it will be successful.

Joe gets up and stretches, "AHHHWAMMM." It almost sounds like a roar. "Hey, I'm getting a soda. Does anyone want anything?" He's angled his words so that his wife will hear him, and he says it loud enough for his friends to hear him also.

"Yeah, Joe get me a popcorn, two large sodas, four hamburgers and a hot dog. Oh, I almost forgot I don't have any money," one of them replies.

"Funny dork, do you want anything? I'll treat." His buddy shakes his head and laughs.

Joe gently touches his wife's shoulder, "Honey, anything for you?"

"No thanks. I'll just have a little of yours."

The teams have already begun their second half warm-up drills when Joe gets back to the bleachers. "I felt like I had a straight jacket on down there," he says. "My elbows were pinned to my ribs and I couldn't move them. With all of the pushing and shoving, it was like a concert crowd, but without the band. You guys are lucky

I came back alive," he exaggerates.

There's someone new on the end of the bleacher, so he has to scoot by sideways, "Sorry."

He wedges next to his wife and the new person. Leaning forward to his friends, "You guys are lucky I'm such a soft touch."

After setting his drink down, he opens the jumbo bag of peanuts and hands them to Izzy, "Here, Izzy take some of these and pass them around, OK?"

"Thanks honey," she gives his knee a squeeze before she grabs the bag with two hands. Virginia, salted peanuts in the shells are her favorite.

With five minutes left in the third quarter Joe's yelling, "Did you see that? I can't believe that he got it away and we scored! That was the greatest play of the game. That was just awesome." After the kick the Cougars were the first on the board with seven points.

His enthusiasm fades a little as the opponents complete a 45-yard touchdown pass as the referee blows his whistle to end the third period. The Cougar's freshman safety fell and the receiver was wide open.

"That's OK guys, you'll get it back," he yells.
A couple of minutes later, the Cougars fumble at their own 23. Their defense holds, but not without giving up a field goal.

The Cougars are trailing by three with only 4:38 left in the fourth quarter. Joe finishes his soda and starts to crunch on the ice. The little squares of coldness are refreshing on this hot night. Joe continues to munch on the ice subconsciously while watching the action on the field. He picks his waxed concession cup up and tilts it towards his mouth. Nothing. He looks in the cup and sees that all the ice is gone except for one cube at the bottom.

He shakes his cup again and holds the cup to his

lips, just a trickle of diluted soda. He shakes his cup more vigorously in a circular motion to try to free the stubborn piece of ice, still no luck. He's determined to get that last piece. It's either him or the ice.

He gives one big clean shake and is momentarily distracted by the play on the field. The Cougars have just completed their third first down of this drive. He looks back in his cup and the chunk of ice is gone. Joe looks at his feet and the surrounding bleachers and doesn't see it. Just as he is about to give up, he notices that the cube has landed in the lap of the gentleman next to him-AHHHHH.

Joe stares in disbelieve. Look at it there. A cube the size of a quarter. Joe thinks that he couldn't have placed it in a worse spot if he had wanted to. It sits there directly on the guy's zipper. "Oh no," he mumbles.

Joe quickly dismisses the idea of a stealth move by which, he would gingerly take his finger and thumb and remove the ice without anyone noticing him. The image of being caught bent over a stranger's lap with his fingers on his crotch is just too embarrassing. Joe shivers and he discounts that plan immediately.

The easiest course of action would be no action. He doesn't know this guy and the guy may think that he had a "control" problem. No one saw Joe and he could easily just ignore it. There's even a very good chance that the guy will move and the ice will fall.

In the end, Joe gently nudges the guy and points with his eyes at the gentleman's lap. His neighbor looks down and immediately notices the chunk of ice.

"Sorry about that buddy," Joe tries to explain. "It kinda got away from me."

The guy chuckles and swipes the little cube to the ground below his feet.

"That could have been a little embarrassing," the

guy says," I'm just happy that you told me. It would have been a little discomforting to get up after the game and have everyone staring at my lower half."

He sticks his hand out and says, "My name's Buddy."

"No kidd'n," Joe says smiling.

"No kidding."

"Well Buddy, it's nice to meet you. My name is Joe. Did you go to school here?"

"No, I've just moved to the district from out of state. I was transferred about eight months ago. My little girl made the cheerleading squad." Buddy explains. He then points to the mass of pompoms and sweaters with an embroidered Mountain Lion on them and says, "She's right there with the blond hair."

Joe has no idea which one she is, but nods his head and says "Oh yeah. Cheering takes a lot of talent and fitness."

Joe continues, "Well you'll love this school. It has more computers than IBM and the teachers are great."

They chat a little more before the roar of the crowd stops their conversation. The Cougars are on the on the six-yard line with the completion of the last pass.

"Hey, what just happened?" Joe asks. Everyone is yelling and cheering, so Joe doesn't get a recap. The offense is in hurry up mode because there's only 49 seconds left. They run down the field and set up quickly. The ball is snapped and it's a quick toss to the wide out. Incomplete.

Second and goal.

"Come on guys, you can do it," Joe's voice is a little rough from all the yelling.

The Cougars line up in the power formation and give it to the fullback who fights for two yards. They quickly call their last time out. He keeps looking from the field to the scoreboard. Joe says nothing and thinks. After almost two hours of watching this team Joe knows what he would do. He would go for the win here. The new quarterback is good enough.

With third and four, the Cougars roll to the wide side of the field and the defense commits to the run. The quarterback squares to the line of scrimmage and lightly tosses the ball into the end zone over the heads of the charging defense. He's leveled after he releases the ball, but the receiver easily tucks it into his belly for the touchdown.

The Cougars win 14 to 10.

Joe says, "Izzy, that was a GREAT game," as they get into their car to go home. "The Cougars really hung in there. I didn't think they had a very good chance at winning at first, but they played strong. I just hope that they play that hard for the rest of the season."

Chapter 5

simplest things

Bills, "The demonstration with Care Free Leisure went great. After I talked to you, I spent the next hour trying to understand what Care Free had told me and what you had said, Joe. You know sell them two units. You had struck a cord. I liked the idea of baby steps and migrating them into the right equipment."

"Which by the way, I laughed later about your comment of not sharing the strategy with them. You're a hoot."

Joe doesn't say anything. He just sits there in the front seat of Bills' car as they go to their first appointment. Bobbi has instructed them to team up to blitz their territories and canvas for new opportunities. Joe likes Bills' car even though it's older than Joe's, it is always clean and glistening. Joe reminds himself to ask what Bills puts on his leather seats and dashboard.

Bills proceeds as if he is describing a natural series of events like putting your socks on before your shoes. He has the uncanny ability to make it sound so obvious and natural. "Their real desire was to get to the point where they could customize all of their material to their clients' demographics and buying habits. The problem was that they needed a solution in a hurry. You know you can't just throw together a bunch of hardware and some software and hope that it works. You have to take your time and be methodical. Furthermore, they wanted an implementation with the least amount of disruption as soon as possible. The whole thing got in the weeds quickly."

"I didn't think that they were going to even listen to my proposal until I started to present your migration ideas."

"I explained to them that we needed to just review hardware for their copying requirements to ensure that we didn't overlook anything. Then we would study their future needs. I was very frank with them about not slamming a box in the account just to get a quick sale. Well that led to further discussions about what they really wanted to do. I'm still not sure that we have all the right people at Care Free involved, but it has helped me cement our relationship. All the other vendors immediately recommended solutions that were not as comprehensive or as customer centric as they needed to be. Personally, I don't understand how anyone could have recommended anything on such short notice. I believe I must uncover the customer's true CBRs."

Confused Joe asks, "Did you say CPR?"

"No, Joe I didn't. I said C B R. That's short for Critical Business Requirements. You know the heart of a company, not just the first requirement that they mention."

Bills continues," Let me explain a bit more, at Care Free they want to maintain their customers, so they can increase their market share. To do this, their marketing plan was for greater personalization of mailing material, but they couldn't do that unless they developed a database of existing customers. Once everything was in place, they asked for Acme, me, to help them. I wasn't just satisfying their copier needs, I was building their market share. Do you get it?"

Joe nods his head and says, "Yeah, I guess I do. But how did you recommend a solution that was appropriate?"

"I haven't yet," Bills states defiantly.

Joe turns his head from the window and studies Bills. He has both hands on the wheel and his back is as straight as a board, but surprisingly he looks relaxed. "What do you mean you haven't given them a recommendation yet? What are you going to let them do, pick their own software?"

Wincing and shaking his head, he briefly stares at Joe before he returns his concentration back to the road. "When Care Free came into the demonstration, I simply explained to them that in order to have a complete understanding of their workflow and their requirements, we needed to discuss at length their ultimate objectives. I was NOT in a position to make a recommendation that would affect their image and ultimately their income without uncovering every bottleneck and barrier."

"We sat for several hours before I finally got around to showing them the 752F and its features. I guess they liked what I said and what I didn't say because they called Bobbi the next day to say what a good rep I was."

"Now get this. I suggested to them to send an email to each department head asking for their input. The results have been great. Not one person's response has been close to any other's. So, if we had gone ahead with a comprehensive software recommendation, I'm sure it would not have been correct. Paul even showed me some of the proposals from the other vendors so that I can review their merits."

"Paul wanted my help. He removed all the pricing figures from the copies of their proposals that he showed me, though."

"There were some good ones, but they all missed the mark when they forgot to engage the different departments. Every department in that company uses different software and in some cases they even use different hardware. Did you know that most marketing departments use a Macintosh computer for their graphic artists?" Bills interrupts himself with that question.

"I guess that would be right, although I really haven't spent that much time in those types of areas," Joe replies.

"Anyway, that meant we had to take a closer look at their critical documents. But more importantly we needed to look at their databases and file sizes. I think we can do what they want. The implementation won't be easy and the transition might be a little painful, but the results should be worth it."

"Did you get the 752F sale?" Joe asks.

Absently, Bills says, "Oh that, yeah, I got the verbal and I'll be picking up the paperwork tomorrow."

Joe, "How were your margins?"

"Oh they were good, but the real Coup de Gras was that Paul and the IT director didn't even approach the other vendors after their visit. It's funny because I thought I would be slowing the sales cycle down with all this talk about solutions, but in fact I was able to qualify my position and showcase Acme's strong offerings."

Joe, "You really think that talking about futures is the right thing to do?"

"No Joe, I wasn't selling futures to Care Free. I was trying to get them to realize that they needed to look at all of their requirements before an integrated solution could be offered. I was not going to be forced into recommending a solution that wasn't fully evaluated."

Bills frowns a little and thinks before he continues.

"Let me explain it a different way. If I asked you to tell me how you get from your house to the office, could you do that?"

"Sure, I hop onto the 202 heading south and get off at Washington," Joe answers.

Bills, "Then what do you do?"

"I go over to Pharmic and make a right. From there it's a straight shot to the office complex."

Bills again asked, "Why do you go all the way down to Pharmic? If you turn right a block earlier onto Shore Drive it's a 'straight shot' to the office, isn't it?"

"Boy, Bills I'm surprised you're not late more often? From Shore Drive I have to wait at that left-hand turn signal. That's the light where maybe only three cars can get through at a time," Joe's voice is triumphant.

"I see, so you travel the extra block so it's a right turn into the complex. Is that right?" Bills questions.

Joe smiles, nods and says, "Right as rain."

Bills, "Now is that the way you ALWAYS go?"

"I've done it enough that I know all the short cuts and that's the fastest way. Trust me."

Bills, "So last year when the water main broke on Pharmic and they were repairing it for three weeks you continued to turn there?"

"Come on Bills, you know that was a nightmare. Traffic moved at a snail's pace. I was forced to go the other way."

"What would have happened if you didn't know the other route? You would have been stuck in that snail's pace traffic, right?" Bills comments.

"Yeah, but that's a once in a while problem, not my regular commute every day."

for a short while and then asks, "I know, it was kind of a trick, but let me ask you this. Do you always get on 202 at the same exit or do you use different ramps depending on the morning rush hour?"

"I usually get on at Delmark if it's before 7:15 and I use the Cactus ramp if I'm running a little late. Wait a second, I see what you're doing, and it isn't going to work. Ninety percent of the time I take the same route to work. You never told me I had to tell you every way that I commute to work," Joe defends.

Bills thought Joe would have caught on a little sooner, "Joe wait, wait, let me explain. I am only using this as an example of why I started to ask Care Free some very basic questions. We all have preconceptions about our customers and their needs. As the tenure of the salesperson increases, so do those perceptions. Most of the times we're right because of our years of experience in the trenches, but as the industry changes and our products change, so too must our biases. I don't have all the answers anymore. The truth of the matter is, I've never had all of the answers. And it kills me to think my years of experience don't mean anything."

"But you know what, Joe? It is precisely those years of experience that I draw on to recreate my sales' skills. Could you imagine coming into this business without our knowledge and history? The competition would chew us up and spit us out. It would be the equivalent of performing surgery without any schooling. Think how many times a doctor has to go back and learn about new drugs and procedures."

"Our opinions and activities may not be a life and death scenario, but we do affect the way businesses operate and what we suggest can affect the profitability of our customers. I have actually become rejuvenated with this new core philosophy. Guess how big the opportunity is at Care Free now?" Bills doesn't wait for the answer. "It's almost twenty times larger then just one or two machines. That's almost my entire budget!"

For the next few miles both of the men are silent as they contemplate their jobs. Bills is excited and motivated while Joe is frustrated and struggling. Just before Bills swings into the customer's parking lot he dials his voice mail.

"Do you have time for a call?" Joe asks.

"I'm just checking my voice mail. If I have a message that I need to return, I'll do it between calls unless it is an emergency then I'll call the customer back immediately."

"I hate wasting my minutes. I normally check my messages twice a day." Joe answers to the unasked question.

Bills finds a spot toward the back against a red brick building with the oversized faded Army logo "Be All that You Can Be." Joe looks at it absently and starts to get out of the car when Bills says to himself, "Good, no problems only happy customers."

"Hi," both Joe and Bills chime at once. They chuckle as they walk to the receptionist.

Bills just stands in front of the circular desk and waits for her to look up before he proceeds. She's reading Woman's Day magazine. Immediately, Joe sees a striking resemblance to the First Lady Laura Bush except this woman is slightly younger. Their hair is cut in the same fashion and is parted on the left. The receptionist's hair has a little more visible gray than the First Lady's auburn hair. Their features are almost identical though. Both women have that smooth face with high cheekbones and a broad thin smile.

She finally inclines her head and acknowledges

them, "How can I help you?"

Bills takes the lead since they are working in his zip code, and he has made the appointment. "Hi, my name is Bill Hamilton and my friend here is Joe Sails. We're here to visit with a Mr. Albright. Is he available please?"

The receptionist is very suspicious and let's them know that she's in charge. "What's this in regard to?"

"We're from Acme and we have a 9:00 o'clock appointment," Bills' words are coated in honey.

She snaps back, "Have a seat while I see if I can locate him."

"Thank you very much." Joe isn't sure if Bills is toying with her or not. But Joe's respect for the receptionist bottoms out and he concludes that while there may be some similar features between her and the First Lady, she will never truly measure up with an attitude like that.

As they take their seats in the lobby, Joe turns to Bills and whispers, "I've had colds that were warmer then her." Bills can't control himself and bursts out laughing which of course rewards him with an icy stare from the not so old "gray mare." Joe acts stupid and looks from his friend back to the receptionist and shakes his head.

By 9:15 they are in front of Phillip Albright, the purchasing manager. The office is small. There are only three chairs - two in front of the desk and a swivel chair behind the desk. The office seems even smaller because of all the boxes in the office. There are boxes stacked along the walls, even the wall behind his desk. Joe can see that they are paper boxes that look to be full because they are only stacked five high, but each stack is perfectly straight. It would stand to reason that if the boxes were partially empty, they would be stacked much higher. If they stacked them to the ceiling behind the desk, people wouldn't have to brush against them as they entered and left this office. It would also make the office look bigger. He wonders if this was actually a storage closet that they converted to an office.

After the handshakes and introductions Bills begins, "Mr. Albright, thank you for seeing us today. As I said on the phone I wanted to introduce myself and get a feel for what your company does."

Bills sits with his legs crossed and has his planner resting comfortably on his thigh. His planner is open to a clean sheet of paper. His hands are folded and he looks perfectly at ease.

"First, I'd like to apologize for the mess," Mr. Albright says, "We're in the process of moving and we ran into a little snag with the new location. It seems as though the site manager forgot to install the appropriate heating and air conditioning ductwork. The units and vents are big enough, but the pipes are too small. I've got an emergency department head meeting in a couple of minutes to map out a strategy."

Since Bills didn't address Mr. Albright by his first name Joe figured he should not also. Joe says, "Mr. Albright, I take it that you have to get out of this building then?"

"That's right, by the way, please call me Phil. We have been negotiating with this landlord to continue to rent this space, but he, of course, has a deadline with the new tenants moving in, " Phil replies.

Both Joe and Bills nod at the predicament that Phil is facing. Looking to gain some common ground with the customer Joe says, "I guess you won't be using those contractors again?"

Phil surprises them both with, "I'm not so sure about that. They have been very accommodating. So much so that they have offered to let us store boxes at their location if we need to. To tell you the truth, this may be our own internal mistake. Personally, I like to work with people that don't automatically go in a defensive mode and start pointing fingers."

Bills' first words that he writes are "vendor commitment."

"They are very professional and, uh, accommodating."

Phil starts a fresh idea with, " OK. As I stated on the phone, I am already committed to your competitor, although that is now on the back burner because of this moving fiasco."

"I know that you have had a strong relationship with them and I just wanted you and I to start a dialogue. If nothing else, it may help me to understand how to support my customers better. Can you tell me the four things that you like most about my competition?" Bills inquires.

"Yeah sure. First, I like the fact that they are very responsive. The second is that their machines are high quality. And their prices are good. Let's see that's three, so I would guess that the last item would be...let's see, uh, oh, I've been dealing with them for a long time."

Bills simply writes three words, "responsive," "quality" and "price."

"I know I've got my work cut out for myself if I am ever going to win your business," Bills states matter-of-factly. "When you talk about responsiveness can you describe the targets that they're setting?"

Phil, "The technicians are here within two or three hours of a call being placed. Most of the time they have the copiers running the same day."

Bills is silent for a moment before he asks, "Would you say they are as responsive as your heating and air people?"

"Not quite that responsive, but they call me. Like a couple of weeks ago they called to discuss the move."

"That's what all salespeople should do - focus on the customer and be proactive in all communications. I pride myself on being customer centric." Bills jots a note about "home."

"Quality was your next item. Had you heard of Acme before and our product lines?"

Phil nods while a quick smile crosses his face and disappears. He thinks that Bills will go on a tangent of how great his company is or all the quality awards that they've won. He may even talk about specific products and test results. So he smiles quickly and waits.

"Great, you know quality is like beauty and it is in the eyes of the beholder. So, I'm not going to bore you with any trumpet statements or anything like that. I just want to ask you a question that you don't even have to answer. Have you ever heard of Acme not doing what's right for the customer?"

"All machines go down. That's the nature of the business, but the heart and soul of any company is defined by their dedication to quality support." Bills decides to leave it at that. Joe is listening intently.

"The third item was the price. I've been doing this for ten years and I have never met a customer that wanted to pay more money for the same identical product. As a salesperson, it is my job to differentiate my company and my products from the competition. And that difference is either going to cost more or less than what you expect to pay."

Again Phil is nodding his head, but this time he does not have a knowing smile on his face. He is thoughtful and intrigued by the mere fact that these two salespeople in his office aren't selling. They're not making grand promises with little to back them.

"Phil, I'm not the cheapest. But, I also won't roll a box in here just to make a sale either. I believe in adding value by thoroughly understanding your workflow and applications. I hope that one day you will view Acme like you view your other vendors."

"Oh the last item was your long relationship with your current vendor. I lose on that one. So I guess I'll have to get cracking on the other three."

Phil motions for someone to come in. Both Bills and Joe start to turn in their chairs when a gentleman says, "Sorry, I just wanted to remind Phil that the meeting is in five minutes."

"Thanks Stephen, " Phil replies. "Look guys I'm sorry I have to run you off, but I've got to make this meeting."

"Phil that's fine. We understand. I'll drop a note to you in the next day or so, and I would like you to come to our open house at the end of next week. We're showcasing our network devices that can streamline most customers' office processes," says Bills.

"Well I can't comment if I can be there, but I'll try. You know you're going to have a battle on your hands to win me over."

"I know, but can you do me one favor please? Read the back of my card when you get a moment."

As the two salesmen are leaving the office, the receptionist is still sitting, guarding the front door as if the Holy Grail is hidden in the building somewhere. Bills, the consummate professional easily says, "Thanks," and "I'll see you soon."

She doesn't even bother to look up. Joe guesses she is reading some intriguing article about next season's shoe styles.

In his car, Bills stops long enough to put a reminder in his Palm while he checks his messages via the hands-free option on his phone. Joe is rustling the sports page to find an article on his Cougars.

Minutes later they are a few blocks down the street approaching Joe's blitz customer. Joe, "Hey, why did you ask Phil to look at your card?"

"Oh, I always hand write my cell and home number on the back of my cards along with the after hours times that I can be reached. I usually put 'available from 7am to 8pm Monday through Saturday'."

Joe is genuinely surprised, "Are you crazy? How many times do you get annoying customer calls at home?"

Bills, "I may be crazy, but only as crazy as a fox. I seldom get calls after hours because most people don't want to take work home with them, so they call me before they leave which is 5:00 o'clock. Secondly, what did Phil say that I had to do to win the business?"

"That's easy," Joe recites, "Service has to be responsive, the price has to be cheap, quality products, and a long term relationship."

"Honestly, Joe have you ever met any customer that didn't want the first three of those items? If I'm buying steaks at the market or if I'm buying a new CD burner, I have the same basic concerns. Although service in a grocery store is customer service, hopefully not repair service. I think you would call the latter salmonella."

"Now, let's take this customer one step further on this logic train. Assume there is a train with five or six towns that it stops at. Since there is only one set of tracks the train must stop at each town before it can proceed. If at any point the townspeople put up a barrier, the train stops dead in its tracks, and the journey ends."

"Let's assume that today's visit was the first town and we passed through it. We still have to get to the other towns, which are responsiveness, quality and price."

"Phil's first concern was responsiveness. I cannot show service's responsiveness without first having equipment in his office. How many vendors do you think Phil sees in a week that says, 'my service is second to none?' To have Phil look at how responsive Acme is I have to be quick to respond myself. My minimum commitment is always the customer's expectation. Phil's perception of his service is that they respond within two or three hours. I'll bet that the actual response time is closer to four or five hours. But the fact still remains that Phil THINKS it is two or three. My response time to Phil's messages will be two hours or less." Bills tries to explain further. "If I don't shine on this one item the rest will never come to pass because our train will be stopped dead in its tracks."

"I have to earn the right to go to the next town with each and every customer," Bills concludes.

Joe sets the paper down and doesn't comment.

The building is a sparkling blue, reflective window structure that's at least six stories tall. Bills pulls into the catacombs that some people call parking lots and gingerly maneuvers round several blind hairpin turns until he reaches a spot near the elevators. P3 is written on the nearest column.

"I don't know if I could do that," Joe finally states. "It would be like I didn't have a life outside of work. And I would just be asking for more headaches."

"Joe, I don't manage you anymore, so you can do what you want. Sales is an easy job if you strive for mediocrity. It is a whole different job if you want to be the best."

Two people are already standing at the elevator when they walk over to it. The up arrow button is lit.

Bills stands and folds his hands around his planner in front of himself while Joe walks over to the panel and presses the up arrow again.

The other people don't take notice. They're in their own thoughts and haven't looked at either of them.

"Joe, have you gone to 'Otis' school?" Bills asks in a good-natured tone.

"What's 'Otis' school?" Joe says a little perplexed.

"You know the school of ups and downs."

"I have no idea what you're talking about."

The two unconcerned individuals are now interested. They've turned their heads and are looking at Bills.

"Oh, I thought maybe you had been trained that if you pressed the button a bunch of times the elevator would come more quickly."

With the slightest of smiles, almost invisible smirks, the two individuals look away.

"I just wanted to make sure that it was properly pushed," Joe straightens his back and thrusts his chin out as he says this.

"I bet you got an A+," Bills' sarcasm is thick.

On the fourth floor the elevator's doors slide open. Both men step out into the hallway and stop. Before them is a huge painting of a vase and flowers. The carpet is plush ivory and the wooden baseboard trim looks to be cherry.

"Excuse me," a voice from behind them says.

"Sorry, didn't mean to block you," Joe says apologetically.

The doors close and the two of them are still trying to figure out which way to go. "I think it's right."

"Joe, your guess is as good as mine. Didn't you set this up though?"

"Sure I did, but they just said the fourth floor."

"You'll double check a lit elevator button by pressing it several more times, but you won't ask for directions. Don't you think that's just a little back assward?" Bills comments.

"Let's just go. We don't have time for chit chat."

They head down the right corridor and around a corner. In front of them is the law office of Horsington, Perry and Berry.

"I told you it was right," Joe almost sneers.

"Great, we're now depending on luck and clairvoyance to meet customers. If you ever lose your job maybe you can go to work as one of those guys that guess your weight at the State Fair."

Joe walks through the door and holds it open for Bills. The plush reception area has wood paneling and lots of recessed accent lighting. A statue of Blind Justice is behind the front desk and commands their immediate attention as they approach. The atmosphere and decor are staunch and conservative.

Joe does the introductions, "Hello my name is Mr. Sails and this is my associate, Bill Hamilton. We have a meeting with uh, uh, (Joe temporarily forgets his contact's last name) so he blurts out only her first name, Ruth. Is she available please?"

"Let me check. What time is your consultation?" the receptionist inquires.

Joe has regained his composure and memory, "Oh we're from Acme and Ms. Scornbac wanted to discuss her office equipment needs."

Receptionist smoothly adds, "I'm sorry I thought you wanted Ruth Legit. She's our lead council for the tobacco litigation. Ruth Scornbac is our office manager. Please have a seat and I'll ring her extension."

Joe smiles and says, "Thank you very much."

Joe and Bills sit comfortably and chat quietly

about Bills' car. They haven't even completed their conversation on leather cleaning supplies when they are directed to Ms. Scornbac's office.

She is a stout woman of about fifty with graying straight hair, cut short-just past her ears with short bangs. It contrasts nicely with her bronze complexion. She's wearing little makeup and calmly sits behind her desk with her hands lapped over each other. She doesn't move when they walk in.

Joe, "Hello, Ms. Scornbac, my name is Joe Sails and I'm from Acme. We talked on the..." He's cut off almost immediately.

Ms. Scornbac barely flicks her hand as if she is swatting an irritating fly and says, "I know. I agreed to the appointment. Who are you?" she hurls the question at Bills.

"I'm sorry, my name is Bill Hamilton. I'm an associate of Joe's."

"No need to be sorry, just take a seat please and I'll tell you what I need."

In unison they both say, "Thank you." They share a quick glance at each other and each is silently dreading the next half hour.

"Gentlemen, I have allowed you to interrupt my day because I am currently looking at replacing our office equipment," she states clearly and precisely.

"Thanks. Great, I'm sure we can be of help," Joe interjects and smiles warmly.

Ms. Scornbac's intense glare freezes Joe's smile. He's not sure if he should apologize for possibly interrupting her or to just shut up. After an eternity, he feels his facial muscles continuing to force that warm smile. He looks down at his notepad, so that he can break her gaze and change expressions.

"As I was saying. We here at Horsington, Perry,

and Berry are in need of equipment." She pauses as she retrieves a folder labeled in blue "reprographics project". She pulls out two identical sets of legal-size documents and hands them over to her guests. Centered on the front of Joe's set is his name. In the lower left-hand corner is the Horsington, Perry and Berry color logo. Today's date is in the lower right-hand corner. Bills' cover sheet to his set is similar, but does not have his name on it. He wonders if she had more than one extra set.

"As you can see our needs are great. At the bottom of the page is a list of machine features: speeds, stapling, document feeders, etc. I expect all vendors to meet or exceed these minimum expectations. I will contract these machines for only three years and want the total cost of ownership on a rental basis and a lease option. Is that understood?"

Both gentlemen feel compelled to nod their heads while answering, "Yes."

"Good. On the second and third pages, there are questions about service and your company that must be filled out completely and accurately. My due diligence has uncovered that Acme has reorganized recently and that their share prices have fallen substantially." She gazes at both men and expects no explanation.

"The last section will be for any special items or considerations that you may want to include."

She waits only a few seconds before plunging ahead again, "Gentlemen, you may read the details later. Do you have any questions for me now?"

Joe decides not to be a wallflower on this one and sets the tone. His years of experience have trained him to know when to act and when to retreat. He just retreated for the last ten minutes, now he has to prove to Scornbac that he knows his stuff.

"Ms. Scornbac, I do not see the locations indicated here?"

"That's correct Mr. Sails. I don't want my people in the various departments being harassed by the vendors!"

Joe is unaffected and he continues, "I can appreciate that. But, Acme can offer you better prices if we know that all the units were in this building for instance, rahter than if they were spread across the city."

She nods her head slowly, "No other vendor has asked for that. I'll see if I can supply details around that for you. For the time being let me clarify. This firm has eighteen locations. Most of this exercise is for this location, but we reserve the right to expand all contracts to include our entire organization."

"Thank you. I was also wondering why you have not listed the existing equipment for trade-in? That may lower your costs."

"We do not own our current machines."

"Oh, I see. Who's your current vendor?" Joe tries to slip this question in.

"The current vendor has no bearing on this new procurement process."

Joe, "I do not want the vendor's name for comparison purposes, but rather to understand your current integration level. Maybe I should put the question this way, 'Are there opportunities to streamline your operations?' You know, not all companies are created equal."

"Yes, of course I realize that. That is why I included the section at the back of your package," her tone is unforgiving.

Joe backs down a little and tries a different approach. The ski trip is swooshing through his mind. "You're looking for replacements for your existing copiers with no additional capabilities?"

"I'm reviewing all offers, but a copier is a copier, right?"

"Well, pretty much, but that's not always exactly right. Uh, would you be willing to review our machines?" Joe asks hesitantly.

"Yes, I believe that would be the most prudent course to take."

"Good, Thursday we will be showcasing our newest copiers. It will be an ideal time for you to 'kick the tires,'" Joe adds. He immediately regrets that comment because it sounds like he's a used car salesman.

"I'll have to check my schedule. Please call me tomorrow at 9:00 to confirm."

"Uh, sure I can do that."

Bills speaks for the first time, "Ms. Scornbac, this is a very thorough document. You'll find that Acme is just as thorough." His comments are to build Acme's credentials in a non-threatening way.

"That remains to be seen Mr. Hamilton."

As they leave her office, they exchange cards and say their good byes.

There's no chatting as they stand at the elevator doors. Joe doesn't push the already illuminated down button. Both are silently comparing this call to other tough customers. Joe thinks that this was by far the most difficult first call he has had since Get It Write Printing several years ago.

Everything was going great with that call. The manager was interested and he was already talking about lease options when the owner walked in. Joe had not realized that the owner was actually a former employee of Acme's. His name was Roger Marcem. When Joe was hired, he took Roger's territory. Roger wasn't happy then and he certainly wasn't happy to see

Joe in his shop. The guy was swearing and cursing so loud that his employees were embarrassed. All the customers turned to see what the commotion was all about. Joe quickly exited.

The problem was that he forgot to pick-up his planner. He had left it in the shop. Ten minutes later, he was entering the battlefield again. So Joe was lambasted twice! Boy was that tough.

Bills also thinks that the call was very difficult. Calls like that are never easy and slow a rep down. But he does realize that some of his toughest initial calls have developed into his strongest allies. You just have to be even more diligent and focused than usual. These types of customers are always looking for an excuse to throw back at you. As a professional you cannot give them that ammo.

The doors slide open and they step on the elevator with another passenger. As soon as the doors close, Joe says, "Boy was she a bear or what? I hate to say this, but I'll probably let this one slip. Even if we win the business," Joe elongates and mockingly says, "Ruuuuthhh will make my life miserable."

"Joe, let's think about this and talk about it later," Bills says as he gestures with his eyes to the gentleman behind them.

Joe quickly catches on. He tries to smooth his earlier comment, "I bet I just need to get to know her."

In the car, both men compare thoughts on the call. Bills tries to convince Joe to withhold judgment until after the open house.

Chapter 6

open house

The last time Bobbi had seen all her team in the office this early was when the divisional president was here nine months ago. She's glad she mandated that all sales and support be in the office by 8:00 when there's an open house day. The event doesn't start for another two hours, but there are a lot of chores to do between then and now. All the big issues have been addressed earlier in the week like assignment of responsibilities and servicing of equipment, but there's still lots to do.

Bobbi enters the demo room and sees four of her sales people in the corner talking loudly and two of the support specialists at one of the computer terminals talking to Bills. She walks to the larger group and says, "Morning guys."

A couple of them raise their coffee mugs and others greet her. Joe says, "Morning Bobbi, your show going to be a success today? I hope so, I have five big customers coming in and want them wowed."

"Don't worry, Joe my middle name is WOW!" she jokes. "You guys look good, but why are you in the corner? Did you do something that you weren't suppose to and Tom sent you here?"

Always the defiant one, Joe quips, "We were discussing strategy. And who was going to have the most customers today."

"Well that's great guys, but let's shake a leg and get this place shipshape. We still need to set up the table and get the silverware out along with name tags, the sign-in book, a message on the marquee...," she mentions a number of other items before she stops.

She looks at the group and can see that no one is going to offer to do anything, so she decides to delegate, "Josh, you take care of the marquee and name tags. Please make sure that our showcase theme is stated clearly. Joe, I want to get going on the tables and I want five fresh pots of coffee ready when the customers get here." She adds as a confirmation, "I know how much you like to make coffee."

Bobbi leaves the group as they disperse and walks to Bill Hamilton.

"Hey guys. Whatcha up to?" she greets.

"Oh nothing," is Bills' sly reply. "Do we look like we're up to something? Tom, you up to something?"

"Why no, Mr. Hamilton, I'm not up to anything. Are you up to something?" He repeats back to Bills.

"OK now I know YOU'RE up to SOMETHING. Spill the beans boys," she says in rebuttal.

Bills, "Well if you must know. We think we have just come up with a way to make this open house very personalized. We're going to have each customer's name in this database," Bills points to the CRT, "and when we send jobs to each of the printing devices, the cover sheets will have the customer's name and Acme's logo. It will be all done behind the scenes and will be very transparent to each of the participants."

Tom adds, "It will seem as though we are creating the sample just for them. These won't be just any old samples either. We're pulling together Acme information along with their vertical market information.

The third person in the group, Andrea, finally chimes in, "Each set will be describing Acme and our strengths."

Bobbi, "This sounds great! But what will happen to those customers that tag along with another person and we weren't expecting them?"

"That's easy, everyone will be directed to sign-in. And then we'll have Louise type their names in this database along with these other fields," Bills says in minimizing the concern. "This should be very impressive."

Bobbi, "I think you're right. Thanks for the second effort." She walks back to her desk and wonders how much over plan she would be if all of her salespeople were that effective.

At 8:30, Bobbi has everyone gathered in the demo room to go over the agenda and to make any last minute changes. There are more than 40 people present with all of the system support people, service managers and some of the technicians plus all of the salespeople. She addresses the group as though it is her bi-monthly sales meeting.

Her first comments are a quick thank you for all of the attendees and then the motivational comments about making this the best open house ever. At the conclusion of the two-minute spontaneous pep talk, she asks if everyone is ready and tries to charge them up with, "I have all the confidence in the world in each of you." But she doesn't quite say it with enough emotion.

That's when Wally, the local service manager, asks to address the group. He pulls out a few index cards and walks to the front. He is a small man of 5' 6" and only 140 lbs. His words are thoughtful and riveting.

At the end of Wally's short speech every person in that room feels electrified and eager to make this event successful. While the setting is very informal and impromptu his words flowed easily and with confidence.

"Hey Wally, that was great," Bobbi says as she walks up to him. The crowd has dispersed and everyone is busying themselves with last minute tasks.

"Thanks Bobbi," Wally is beaming. "I put these words together earlier in the week and rehearsed them."

"Well it certainly showed. That was a very inspirational …uh, motivational speech. I wish I could talk like that in front of a group."

"You can, you just have to want to. No offense, but I bet that you didn't even consider the words you were going to say. You knew what you wanted to say, you knew the content, but you probably just winged it this morning. Since I didn't see any prompts, I'm going to also assume that you didn't practice either."

"No. You're right, but I do this so often that it's second nature to me," Bobbi admits.

"Then why did you think mine was so good? Or were you just throwing me some fluff?"

"No, it was good," Bobbi states. "I just don't think I could be that convincing."

Wally adds, "Bobbi I've got to run, but let me say one thing. It is our responsibility to be more than just managers. We need to be leaders. We need to instill the passion in our troops. They're not going to get it from each other or from our stock price. We have to be the ones who are the field marshals. It is our responsibility to motivate them."

"Hey I've got to run to this conference call. We'll talk later if you want, OK?"

Bobbi, "I'd like that because I think you can give me a few pointers. I guess I've been in robot mode. You know I've been managing for so long, I thought I was pretty good at it."

"Look Bobbi, I didn't mean to accuse you of doing a bad job. On the contrary, I think you've done a pretty good job here for the last year or so. We all need to be increasing our skill sets. I, for one, am going to work at being a better leader. That means I'm going to have to challenge my preconceived ideas and habits because I've been managing since you were in diapers."

"Come on Wally, you only look old," Bobbi jabs. "Let's have lunch or an early morning meeting in the next week or so, OK? I'll send you an email with a couple of good times for me and all you have to do is circle what's best for you and return it."

"That sounds great Bobbi, because I do need a sounding board." And with that Wally is out the double doors walking rapidly to his office.

Bobbi walks through the demo room. She pulls up the blinds and checks to make sure the windows are clean. She then walks to each station and checks to ensure the units are on. She also takes the liberty of checking behind each unit. She wants to make sure that there is no trash or any papers that customers may inadvertently see.

Joe pops his head in and says, "Bobbi the coffee's going and I've got the thermoses ready. Do you need anything else?"

"Yeah Joe, check and see who's got demo room responsibility this week. Louise will have the chart."

Joe questions, "We're still doing that? I don't think anyone has been keeping up with it."

"Damn it. Do I always have to check up on everything?" she snaps.

"Don't shoot me, I'm only the messenger. I'll go find out."

"No never mind. I guess I need to inspect that too," she concedes shaking her head wearily.

Joe is standing next to her and starts talking about the customers that are coming and what times they'll be there. He takes a sip from his mug. "That's cold," he remarks and walks over to a beautiful fern in an ornate terracotta planter. To Bobbi's dismay, he casually dumps his remaining coffee in the planter.

She's speechless. Her expression of shock and horror are chiseled in her face.

Joe turns around and sees Bobbi's reaction. "Don't blow a casket Bobbi. Look at all the other plants in here and then take a look at this one. I put a lot of sugar in my coffee and this little guy seems to like it."

Bobbi doesn't say anything, but slowly pans the room and examines all of the other plants. Sure enough this fern is doing the best. She wants to say something negative, but can't think of anything. She shrugs her shoulders and says, "I guess you're right. Do me a favor though, don't let everyone start doing that."

Relieved Joe says, "Bobbi do you know that little tree by my desk? I've been feeding it coffee for six years and it looks like a sequoia. If coffee worked that well on me, I'd be 6' 7" and 280 pounds.

Bobbi's mildly reproaches Joe, "Look Joe it may be good for the plants, but it doesn't make YOU look good. You need to be careful about your image. What do you think other people would say if they saw you throwing your coffee in the planter? 'Joe sure has a green thumb,'" she says sarcastically. "No they'll say that you're 'lazy or inconsiderate.' Worse yet is what they'll think. You have to be careful about your image. An image is very fragile and can be easily tarnished."

She explains further, "That's why I'm in here checking behind machines and looking beyond the obvious because I want to make sure that when customers are in my house they get the right impression."

Joe considers her words and comments, "I guess, you're probably right Bobbi. I'll be a little more respectful of my own image. I'm not trying to change the subject, but I would really like to introduce you to Ruth from Horsington, Perry and Berry. She'll be here at noon. Do you think you'll be available?" he asks.

"Sure Joe. I'm here all day."

As he is walking out the door, Bobbi is still doing her "white glove" test. She doesn't notice that Joe hesitates then bends down to pick up a few fallen leaves from one of the plants.

"Good morning," Louise cheerfully addresses the customers as they walk to her desk.

"Hello, I am Ms. Scornbac and these are my associates. Is a Mr. Sails available please?"

"Yes of course and welcome to Acme." She adds, "Would all of you mind signing in please?" Louise pages Joe over the intercom.

The show has been very busy this morning. Many of the salespeople have had at least two or three customers already come by and look at the equipment. So far all has worked smoothly, including the customized samples. Joe is in the middle of a presentation when he hears the page.

Excusing himself, he pushes back from the conference table and looks at his watch, 11:03. "Tom will you please take over for a minute?"

As Joe walks by the front desk he says, "Thanks Louise."

A couple of steps later he is in front of the small group of women.

"Good morning, Ms. Scornbac. I uh, ...I trust you had no trouble finding our office?" Joe says as a greeting.

He extends his hand and gives her hand a gentle, firm shake.

"Traffic was light, so there were no issues with getting here," she says in reply.

"Great." Joe waits for the introduction to the two other women. Nothing is forthcoming, so he forges ahead, "Ladies my name is Joe Sails and I would like to welcome you to Acme. Thank you for finding time in your busy schedule to view our machines today."

He continues," May I get you anything, coffee, tea or water?"

Ms. Scornbac states in a dry voice, "No thank you. We would just like to see the equipment please."

Joe, "Sure, give me a few minutes please, I'm with another customer and we are just finishing up. Let me see if my boss is available. She may be able to answer any questions that you have until I'm free. Is that OK?"

"I know we're early Joe. I have a very important meeting to attend at one o'clock back in my office. I would like to start the demonstration as soon as possible."

Joe, the consummate salespersons, smiles affably and ensures them that it is absolutely no problem, but it may take a little time to arrange. Inside he's burning at this customer's total lack of consideration.

The last thing Joe wants to do is leave these customers in the lobby like forgotten stepchildren, so he walks to the double doors and holds one of the doors with an outstretched arm. "This way please."

As the women are filing past Joe says, "Louise, would you please ring Bobbi for me? Thanks."

He directs them to the food table where there are only a few items left: onion bagel, cinnamon donut holes and a bowl of fruit. The tablecloth is covered in crumbs and stains where accidents and spills have been recorded.

"Please help yourselves. If you're here at noon we're having sandwiches from The Deli brought in."

For the first time Ms. Scornbac's exterior softens, "Is that the place right around the corner?"

Joe agrees, "Yes, right next to the pharmacy."

"That's my favorite place. I love their oriental salads!"

Joe excuses himself and goes back to Louise's desk. He's relieved to see that no one else is around. "Hey. Any luck finding Bobbi?"

"She's on her way."

"Great, I owe you. I'll buy you lunch today."

"Thanks Joe, you're all heart," she replies, knowing that lunch is catered today.

For some unknown reason, Louise's words strike a cord with Joe. He is a good person at heart. And the words strengthen his resolve not to let Ms. Scornbac affect his actions. "Oh, I did want to get something special for lunch. He reaches over the front of the desk and removes The Deli's menu. Any chance that you can order me one oriental salad Louise?"

"Sure Joe, consider it done."

"Thanks Louise," Joe genuinely responds.

"Bobbi I need your help," Joe pleads as she enters the waiting area. The group from Horsington, Perry and Berry arrived early and I still have a customer in the conference room."

She acknowledges the predicament and says, "This always happens."

"Bobbi, here are the packages that I prepared for them last night. All we're missing is cover sheets with their names on them. I'll introduce you to them and then I need to head back to the conference room, OK?"

Bobbi looks quickly through the folder and is very

impressed. There are a couple of brochures on Acme and the products, but more importantly there is a cover letter with support material about law firms and their challenges today. Joe has even gone to their Website and downloaded some information. Acme and Horsington, Perry, and Berry share some of the same customers.

The admiration in her voice is obvious, "Joe this looks great!"

"Thanks, I copied the idea from Melissa," he divulges.

They both push open a double door and walk directly over to the food table where the customers are standing.

"Ladies, I would like to introduce my boss. This is Bobbi Dunham. Bobbi this is Ms. Ruth Scornbac...."

Ruth Scornbac grabs Bobbi's hand and says, "Please call me Ruth. I'm so glad to see women rising to the top."

Joe's a little stunned. He's not sure if he should be mad or ecstatic. On the one hand Ruth has been very standoffish and prudish. Now though, she seems to have taken an immediate liking to Bobbi. This really may help in the long run. Joe assumes the sale and says, "Ruth you're in great hands, and Bobbi thanks for the help."

He hustles back to the conference room where Tom is still on the same slide as before.

Forty minutes later, Louise is paging Joe again. It's perfect timing because he's returning from the parking lot where he had escorted his original customers. Joe is scurrying by the front desk toward the demonstration room when Louise jokes, "Hey Joe your salad is here. I only had a couple of bites."

"Thanks again for getting this for me. I can always count on you. Have my other customers left yet?"

"No. They're at the table in back of the demo

room." Louise hands the "brown bag" over to Joe.

Joe eyes The Deli sandwiches as he takes long strides by the table. Bobbi is just getting up when Joe arrives. He notices that the binders he had prepared with their names are now in front of them. "Sorry," he offers as an excuse.

Joe could have rushed his other customer along. He didn't. He had decided that he wanted Bobbi to develop the relationship side of this customer. It's in his best interest to let go of his pride and let her help him. Almost like assigning roles. It's why you bring your manager into accounts in the first place. The manager is supposed to help you penetrate higher and deeper within target accounts. He was just allowing Bobbi to take a more active role in the relationship side of things.

The rest of the women are stirring and arranging their documents.

"I guess I missed a little," Joe's comment is meek.

Bobbi consoles him, "If we have time today, I'll debrief you on all that we did and our next steps."

Joe hands the bag to Ruth and says, "We took the liberty of getting you this."

"What is it?" Ruth is a little surprised and starts to peek into the bag.

"Just a salad," he says.

Ruth smiles warmly at Joe for the first time.

He smiles backs. This little gesture of consideration seems to have helped. He proceeds, "When are we going to meet next?"

"Joe I can't say. I still need to talk to the chairman of the committee - Mr. Buddy Wainwright. He'll be deciding when the next meeting is based on his schedule, not mine."

"Buddy as in B-U-D-D-Y," Joe clarifies.

"Yes that is he. Do you know him?"

Speculating Joe says, "I'm not sure. Has he just moved into the area in the last year or so?"

Ruth's voice opens at a warm pitch, "Why, yes. He came from our national headquarters."

"I may know him, but I hope he doesn't remember me." Joe chuckles as he says it, and the women just look at him.

Chapter 7

think

"That wasn't bad at all," Bills says, "Two solid appointments this morning."

"Are you hungry or are you going to drop me off at the office?"

Bills stretches his right-arm over his head and bends it as he brings it down. He then looks at his watch. It's only 11:10. "Let me see what messages I have and then let's go to lunch at noon, OK?"

"I was just hoping to get in and out of lunch quickly today because of the crowds," Joe says as he tries to convince his traveling companion to break early. It's their second travel day together.

"Joe I'd like to, but no can do. I have to get something going. I can't waste any time. If I go to lunch now my customers are still working, so even if I only take an hour, by the time I get back to the office they will still be at lunch. It's not as much of an issue of whether it takes me 30 minutes or 45 minutes to eat lunch; it is a matter of coordinating my schedule with their schedule. It would be like me trying to get in touch with them from 5:00 to midnight. My chances are pretty slim that I would be successful."

"That's a pretty good point." Joe nods his head as he digests this new idea. He's starting to appreciate Bills. Maybe he hasn't been just lucky. He seems to be very perceptive. Joe wonders if he was this smart when he was his boss.

Joe concedes, "OK, yeah that sounds like a good plan. We'll break for lunch at noon."

At the office, they split up for the first time that day and go to their respective desks.

Bills calls Louise and informs her that he is in the office. While he briefly chats with her he starts to connect his laptop to the network. He then checks his messages for the fourth time that day. There's a new one from Corie Wratchet about an issue that she hopes he can help solve. He saves the message after writing her number down.

As he is dialing the number Bills reviews Corie's phone-listing file to make sure that this cell number is in it. "Hi Corie, Bill Hamilton. How are things today?"

"Great, Bill thanks for getting back to me, so quickly," she says.

"Remember Corie, I'm here to make you happy," he jokes. He then adds, "You can always come to me when customer issues are the concern, you know that."

"I wish everyone had your philosophy," she says and quickly gets to the point. "There's an issue at an account I was hoping that you could help me with."

"Sure, go ahead. I'm all ears." And with that he stops reading his email and closes his screen halfway. He knows from experience that if he doesn't focus he could miss something important.

"I'm not sure if it's your account, but…."

Ten minutes later, Bills has completed his note taking and reviews them with Corie to make sure that the facts he has captured are correct. He promises her that he or someone else would be getting back to her as soon as there was an answer.

The problem is that a customer is using generic supplies. Corie believes these supplies are damaging the machine and that someone needs to have a conversation with the customer. Corie has talked with the operators, but they are not the decision-makers, so she's stuck. Even though there have been a lot of changes in the territories lately, Bills is sure that this customer is not his. He encourages Corie to call him if it hasn't been resolved in a week.

He could easily pass this issue to Bobbi and have the monkey off his back, but he doesn't. Corie is now his customer. She deserves the same care and attention that any customer deserves.

Since he is already online he flips up his screen and drafts a four-line email describing the problem. He refers to his notes frequently and suggests that this should be resolved by Friday the 4th. He sends it to the salesperson whom he thinks the customer belongs to and copies in both Bobbi and Corie. He's concise and ends by asking to be included in the resolution. The subject line reads, "Customer Issue".

Bills hates it when he is not sure of what his expectations should be. So he always sets them when dealing with other people. His thirteen year old thinks her father is "WACKED." Bills thinks that all teenagers feel their parents are "WACKED." At home, Bills sets the proper expectations, like "I want the garbage taken out in the next five minutes." Or he may say, "On Saturday I want you to clean your room before your baseball game." He will even write a note on Friday reminding his daughter. His intent is to get the room cleaned not to see if she will forget or not, consequently, there are a lot of reminders.

It's tough though because with expectations, there have to be consequences of non-compliance. That's another way of saying that not doing her chores will result in no IMing, Nintendo or MTV.

Joe goes over to his desk and retrieves his messages for the first time that day. There are already seven from this morning. He's a little distracted as he listens to the fist message from Bobbi. Halfway through his fourth message he hangs up, pushes back from his desk and walks to Bills' cubicle.

He stops right behind Bills' chair to make sure that he isn't on the phone and clears his throat, "Aaggmm."

Twisting in his chair he sees that it's Joe and says, "Didn't I just leave you?"

"Yeah, but I was thinking about something you said, the first day that we traveled together about mediocrity and I was hoping that we could talk more about it at lunch. I, uh, could use a little advice," Joe stammers and admits to Bills.

"Sure, Joe not a problem. Let me finish my emails and then make my five approach calls though, OK?"

"I've got to go talk to Bobbi and then finish my voice mail, too. I should be ready in a half hour."

Joe shoves his hands in his pockets and starts to walk toward Bobbi's office. He's looking down thinking about how he wants to approach the conversation with Bills. You see, he doesn't want to come across as the town idiot, but he also recognizes that after today he is doing something fundamentally wrong. He is so deep in thought that he has walked by Bobbi's door and continues for a few more steps.

Bobbi looks up and sees Joe walk past her door. He's so pre-occupied she thinks that maybe he's on his cell phone. She keeps looking at the empty doorframe, when from the hall she hears, "Oh." Joe enters her office and now she can see that his other hand is also in his pocket.

"What's up champ?" she says as encouragement. "What's on your mind?"

Joe is still a little dazed or contemplative. "Oh, I was just talking to Bills and..."

She interrupts him and says, "Who?" She almost sounds like an owl.

"Bills - Bill Hamilton." He now makes eye contact. "I call him Bills because of all his money. To get on with it, he was talking about the amount of work that is needed to be a good salesperson. He said something like, 'Sales is an easy job if you only want mediocrity. But it's a hard job if you want to be the best.' That hit a nerve with me because I used to be the best and now I'm just an average shmuck."

Bobbi is happy that the first part of her plan has worked so well. She had wanted Joe to relate to Bill and maybe start some friendly rivalry between them. She hadn't planned on it working this quickly or affecting him this deeply. She had been so used to managing by activity that focusing on her customers' true needs-in this case her salespeople-had been lost on her.

Going through the motions of making sure that the results are there is the crux of the problem when times get tough. Anyone can sell water in the desert. That's an easy proposition. The difficult sale is when the water is free, the customer is cutting costs and you're selling bottled water. Too many times, Bobbi has felt that she was just "pushing paper" and filling in squares rather than changing core behavior. You can always make your monthly goal by putting carrots in front of salespeople when the times are rolling.

Today, Acme is not in the mist of good times. The

company has downsized and like every other large corporation, debt reduction and cost controls are taking their tolls. Competition is constantly getting tougher. New leaner companies are entering the market and some of the manufacturers are even now competing with their own distribution channels. The end result is that margins are being squeezed. To add insult to injury the economy is on a downslide. The forecast for the next twelve months is flat at best with most indicators showing corporate America reducing their spending.

Bobbi blames herself for this current situation with Joe. Her manager, Bishop, is yelling for results and his manager is probably doing the same thing. Everyone is watching the end of the race and complaining if we don't win. Sure there are little squares on forms that need to be filled out to make sure the total job is being done. "The Forecaster" is a great example of probably ten different processes that she must inspect and forward up the chain. But, not one of those processes speaks of core behavior in its rawest form.

Take for instance sales activities and "The Forecaster." Bills' prospects in the last year have a much higher percentage of closing than Joe's. Why is that? Is Joe looking through the phone book and just picking company's names out to put in this form or is there something fundamentally different? Joe certainly has proven himself in the past to be a superior salesman. Is Joe slacking or is he running too long in one spot? Have the standards changed around him and he's been left behind? It wasn't too long ago that a customer would wait three or four weeks for a copier to be delivered. Today, when a customer makes a decision they normally want it yesterday.

So, if business has changed and customer's expectations have changed, can Bobbi change Joe's core behaviors? It's obvious that change is needed and that the old methods of managing are not working in this dynamic business environment. She could manage the little squares on her forms all day long and never help Joe to overachieve on a regular basis.

Activities are needed and must be audited, but they should be reviewed only after core behaviors have been internalized and demonstrated by the salesperson. In essence, core behaviors should get the same attention that results do. She believes that she has some of the core behaviors outlined: empathy, desire, attitude, commitment and timely, accurate communications. But how do you get someone to change his or her business personality?

An image crosses Bobbi's mind of her as a stern kindergarten teacher demanding that little Joey share his crayons. "Mr. Joseph Sails, how many times have I told you to share with your neighbors? How would you like it if no one shared with you?" No, Bobbi can't treat these adults like kids. She has to find a method that works. Her first instinct was to list these quality behaviors and then talk about each one separately and the need for internalizing them. But she decides against that method because everyone wants to have these qualities and probably believes that they do have them. The fact of the matter is, that most of the sales representatives that she has ever managed lacked some of these attributes - even the good ones.

"I wouldn't call you a shmuck," she tells him. "I think you have just subconsciously lost your edge."

"My edge? I'm as dull as a butter knife," his voice rises a little.

"I know. Hey you came in here."

Joe's response sounds gloomy, "I'm sorry. This is just eating at me a little, I guess."

"I know that's why I'm here. Do you want to close the door and talk or something?" It wasn't exactly the Wharton School of Business perfect response.

"No, I've got some things that I need to do before I go to lunch with Bills. I just wanted to ask you if we were still on to go to Carroll's late next week?"

"Yeah, I'm committed to this account. I've got all the information that we discussed and I have already received your password for accessing the mainframe, so that you can start retrieving some of this information yourself. Now you can pull your own reports. In our next P&R, I'll show you how to sort the information."

"Great, I'll confirm with you again at the end of this week."

Joe walks out her door to his desk and starts to dial his voice mail again.

Bills and Joe are eating at a greasy spoon downtown.

"Why did you walk to my cubical when we got back to the office to ask about lunch?" Bills asks Joe.

"What do you mean? I wanted to talk to you about having lunch with you." Joe's a little annoyed.

"Why did you WALK to my desk and not call me?" Bills emphasizes. He doesn't stop, but plows ahead. "Use your tools and use them effectively. Your phone is only one of your tools. I'll bet that you don't use your email effectively either."

Joe's barrier-building response is, "I just don't have the bandwidth to handle it all." He crunches on a pickle and continues. "They're trying to get blood out of this turnip."

"We've now traveled together twice, right?"

Joe shrugs.

"Do you know what I do when I come out of an appointment? I check my messages while I am jotting notes in my Palm about the last call. Furthermore, I'm prepared to take notes if I have to react to a message."

"Yeah, so. I'm checking my messages at least twice a day, sometimes more," Joe defends.

"Now remember I am not your manager anymore, so what I'm going to say may seem like a dig, but I just want you to see the difference," Bills says as a cautious introduction. "I did not see you make one phone call the entire morning. I made three. That means I had ten or fifteen minutes more time in the office to do emails or demo preparation, etc. I try never to procrastinate."

"When I used to interview people I would ask this question, 'would you like to have Mondays or Fridays off?' The interviewees were always stunned and perplexed. The general consensus is that people who want to have a Monday off usually procrastinate. People who want Friday off try to complete all their work before they go home for the weekend. Joe, you'll have to ask yourself that question."

"Let me just add one other idea, I always imagine that there is a customer with me at all times. We always shine in front of customers, right? I think I'm at my best when I'm talking to customers. So, I have taken that mindset and I've incorporated it into all of my daily activities. I imagine there is a customer watching me. They can see everything that I'm doing. Would they buy from me if they saw what I do when I walk out of their office? Now the real question is, do you think that this customer would buy from you if they could see everything that you do or don't do?"

Their lunch goes on for a full hour with Joe listening to Bills' philosophies before they go back to the office.

Chapter 8

picture this

Josh is the class clown of the team. He's the one that always has everyone smirking and laughing. Even through all the changes at Acme, Josh hasn't allowed it to affect his attitude. Today his efforts at humor seem to be focused on Joe, although Joe hasn't caught on yet.

It's 4:25 and the 4:30 meeting is just about ready to start. Half of the team is there and Bobbi is at the front of the room preparing for what most of the salespeople believe to be a routine exercise.

Normally, in these bi-weekly meetings she will review the actual numbers (installs and their associated revenues) with forecasted amounts. She will then put the team's forecast amounts against what the actuals are. And finally, she will review the year-to-date results. They focus on actual against team budget. If a sales representative is having an exceptional month or has just closed a big order, she'll recognize them and their efforts. Finally, she'll review all of the communications and important information, so she is certain that everyone has all of the correct pricing, corporate information, etc.

Today's meeting will be a little different.

"Hey Joe nice pictures," Bills says coming into the

conference room.

Joe simply says "Thanks." because he thinks that Bills is commenting about the new pictures on his desk.

A few minutes later Kay walks in and is carrying an 11"x17" color copy of Joe into the meeting. It's a picture of Joe's head crudely placed on top of the body of an oversized mosquito. Under the picture is written, "Pesky little thing, isn't he?"

When she holds up the picture there are definite smudges on the image. "Hey where did you get that?" Joe's surprise is evident.

"It was taped to the floor in front of the restrooms."

Everyone starts to laugh. They are not only laughing at the picture, but also at Joe's indignation. "Who did that?" Joe quickly looks around the room for Josh and misses him as he turns his head from side to side. Josh is slowly inching down in his chair when a voice from the back says," Joe, I saw a lot more of those in the back bathroom. It's a good thing that, whoever did it, used the new water insoluble inks."

"Yeah," another male voice says, "it gave me something to aim at."

With that Joe finds Josh and says, "Paybacks are hell."

He walks out the door to fetch his unauthorized picture extravaganza. Several minutes later, Joe walks back into the conference room, where everyone is still laughing and talking, trying desperately to retain his dignity. His back is as straight as a board and his chin is set. He avoids all eye contact as he sits down and busies himself with getting a sheet of paper out, so that he can take notes.

From behind him someone says, "Hey, Joe I hear you got a new Website for your pictures. Can you give me that URinaL address please?"

There's another uproar of laughter. Bobbi tries to get control, "OK folks, time to get serious. Let's get down to business. Joe do you need some water, you look a little flushed?"

At that, everyone breaks up again. Joe's mettle cracks and he smiles. After several minutes, the ruckus is calmed and they get down to business.

"OK folks, we've got a lot to cover and I want to jump right in," Bobbi begins. "We've been doing this bi-weekly meeting now for the last year. And I think we are getting stagnant. I want to incorporate other measurement processes into what we believe is a successful salesperson other than just the results."

She comes to the side of the pedestal and looks at her sales team. She pans the crowd for several very long seconds. They are equally divided around the horseshoe-shaped conference table with Bills and Joe sitting together at the top of the shoe and her position is at the opening. She drapes her left arm over the top corner of the wobbly stand and casually starts to speak again. "I've been thinking and have come to the conclusion that while results are the ultimate barometer of our financial success," she pauses, "they don't really tell the whole story. We need to get back to doing the right things. We need to act as though what we do is more than just a job. We have no passion to do what's right. We are salespeople folks. And everything we do either supports our efforts or holds us back. I'm not just talking about returning phone calls or seeing customers. I'm talking about EVERYTHING. I'm fed up with the slackers!"

"I did a walk through the demo room before our show and everything looked good at first glance. But when I took a closer look the room was a mess. Paper was shoved behind machines and trash bins were overflowing. I even found a customer order form on a copier."

Josh pipes in, "Can I have it?"

She glares at Josh and then the whole room, "I'm not kidding when I say, and we will be focused."

No one had been expecting this, so no one around the table says anything. This is a turn no one was ready for.

"From now on at these meetings, I'm going to have each of you stand and tell me about a customer centric story for the previous two weeks." She holds up a hand to quiet any comments or moans. She pauses again, looks at Melissa, "I want to hear, not how you beat the competition, but on how you improved our image or your image to the customer. If we are doing the right thing for our customers, the rest will be easy. As a company we can sell boxes without customer focus only a few times before we   start   making   customers unhappy. We HAVE to keep the customer's interests first. And please don't recite week after week your efforts to resolve billing problems. I hope that one of you will stand up one day and tell me how you have avoided any billing problems for a customer. Or how your diligence caught a supply chain issue before it became a customer's problem."

"I'm hoping that in the next six months these customer centric stories will take root and then be standard business practices. As we go forward any improvements can only make our jobs easier, right?"

There's no response from the peanut gallery. So she takes it up a notch and gets a little more passionate.

"Who in here will be a lawyer in six months? Maybe a NASCAR driver?"

"I've seen the way Melissa drives and you never know," Josh offers as he tries again to lighten the mood.

Bobbi lets this one slide. A few sporadic chortles, but everyone is a little confused with Bobbi's comments just as she had hoped. Lunch with Wally had helped her own self-imposed limitations. She had been managing on autopilot and needed to shake things up. She needed to invigorate her group, so she had scripted this meeting to maximize its effect.

"So, we are all sales professionals right? My point is that if everyone on the team is not striving for customer satisfaction then our image, our reputation is then tarnished and consequently our incomes! I for one, cannot find time to do all the work that needs to be done now, so how am I suppose to find time in the future if our reputation falls to the point that I can't get customers to call me back? Our jobs will be twice as hard and we'll earn half as much!"

"I want all of you to take just a moment to think about what you can do better for your customers. This isn't a game and it isn't a new frivolous task. I'm serious and I want all of you to take this seriously. I also want to see on your schedules that you are double-teaming at least a half a day a week. I don't care who you travel with or when, but you need to team up with someone."

"Joe and Bill were together a couple of times in the last several weeks. Both have come to me and said that their blitz days were a huge success. That's why I'm instituting it now. For the next six months, I want to have tandem travel days and customer focused strategy reviews. Does anyone have any questions?"

Melissa, "So we don't have any new forms to fill out or paperwork?"

"No, no additional administrative work. I just want participation. I may talk to you and your team members occasionally or ask to see your schedule. You know to inspect what I expect, but nothing formal."

This was a loud and clear statement that Bobbi would not let this be a one-time event. They were going to travel and she was going to inspect it.

At the end of the meeting Joe approaches Bobbi. "Hey Bobbi, I wanted to tell you again that I really enjoyed riding with Bills last week and I like this new idea. He has been a wealth of knowledge and his support is great."

Bobbi is waiting for the proverbial other shoe to drop.

"Carroll's just called me today and I've got that appointment with them tomorrow. Bills and I are going out there to really figure out what they need. I didn't think that you wanted to do a three-person call, so why don't I just give you some feed back in our P&R?"

Bobbi hasn't changed her expression. Her emotions are exploding inside though. Who does he think he's dealing with? I will not give him the benefit of a knee jerk reaction and I will not back down. Once again, she rationalizes that Joe is her customer and that she must not waver on this one. Joe's defensive mechanism is working overtime. His fear of management oversight probably stems from the fact, that now more then ever he knows where he has been slacking. To bring me in on a sales call can only emphasize his deficits. "Joe, you're right I don't like to do three-person calls. I'll ask Bill if I can go in his place."

"Uh, are you sure Bobbi? I know this is last minute and I sure don't want to put my boss out."

In a tone that is a little more forceful then she was intending, "Look Joe I need to go to Carroll's. Is there an issue with that?"

"No Bobbi, I was just concerned with your schedule and any conflicts."

"I'll work through any conflicts," she says. "What

time is the appointment?"

"They said that we could come by at 11:30."

"How about we meet at the office?" Bobbi asks.

Some of Bills' tenacity has rubbed off on Joe and he clarifies, "Bobbi, no offense, but can we nail it down a little more than that because I have four other appointments on my schedule?"

"Good point Joe," Bobbi is surprised by his comment, but on reflection it's a step in the right direction for Joe. "How about if I meet you in the office by 10:00 and we'll drive over together?"

"OK Bobbi 10:00. See you then." Joe turns and walks around the horseshoe thinking that his luck couldn't get any worse.

As an afterthought Bobbi says, "Hey, Joe I'll just go to all your appointments tomorrow morning with you. I don't have any pressing issues in the morning, so I'll just travel with you till noon." As a show of support she adds, "I'll just get in the office by 7:00 to do some of my paperwork."

At the door Joe doesn't even turn around, but merely nods his head in acknowledgment to Bobbi's comment and says, "Sure." He was wrong about his luck it just got worse.

Bobbi is alone. The conference room is empty and she begins placing the information that she presented back into the folder. She thinks about this whole process of change. She could easily have told Joe that she didn't have the time to travel and concluded that his time being spent with Bills was good enough. That would not have been the correct message. Joe has to feel that she is committed to him and that they are a team. Allowing Joe to have one good action or activity does not constitute core behavioral change. It may only reflect an effort to change. Without diligence and guidance, Joe will fall back to his comfort zone of bad and unproductive behavior without realizing it. Two outcomes could then occur.

First, he may believe that he has changed. This partial or miniscule difference in core competencies will nudge him in the right direction, but since there has not been a true transformation, frustration and failure will continue to plague him. Second, he may become callous to all efforts to change. He'll feel that change is for everyone else and develop barriers that will then be virtually impregnable. Dooming him once again to failure while his competition adapts and excels.

She justifies her additional workload by concluding, "I've done the right thing for my customer - Joe."

The pot is half full as Joe pours himself a cup. He walks past the empty cubicles and hits the light switch for the bank of fluorescent tubes to flicker on. It's 7:23 and he still can't believe his good luck with the traffic this morning. He was out his door at 7:00 sharp. There were no back-ups or delays. Just smooth sailing.

As he is plugging in his laptop he leans all the way back and looks up the alley between the cubicles and sees Bobbi's office light on. He knew she would be in just as she had promised.

They have four customer calls today, and he needs to make sure his ducks are in a row. Bills' words have been ringing in his head all the way from home, "Imagine that you have a customer with you at all times watching." Joe doesn't have to imagine anything because his not so invisible customer today is his boss. Joe sits at his desk and concentrates on getting a few things done. Bills also was adamant on adjusting his schedule to do the least favorable activity first, "That way you won't be walking around under a dark cloud all day." That's easy for Bills to say. Joe's least favorite activity today is his morning travel with Bobbi.

He does need to call the Major back and try to set something up for early next week. His calendar that he will be reviewing with Bobbi doesn't show much in the line of customer face time later in the week. Joe would have bet his last commissions check that Bobbi would have grown tired of this calendar mess after the first four weeks. It has been almost six weeks and she still seems to be going strong. She has not given him any indication that she's losing interest.

"Morning Bobbi, I'm here, but I have a couple of calls to make before we leave. Let's say we beat feet at ten to eight? I don't want to get stuck in here when the others come in," Joe adds.

"Joe just come by my office and I'll stop what I'm doing," Bobbi offers.

Joe hangs up the phone and quickly dials the Major's number. The phone is answered after one ring, "Good morning, this is an unsecured line, Private First Class Terrell." Joe hears the greeting as almost a command.

"Good morning, is Major Burnsides in please?" Joe's voice almost takes on an air of authority.

"No sir, the Major is at PT, may I help you sir?"

"I don't think so. Will you just tell the Major that Joe Sails from Acme called? I'm visiting customers today, but would like to talk with him about setting up an appointment for tomorrow."

Private First Class Terrell's reply is very professional and direct, "May I have the phone number where the Major can reach you, please?" Joe almost hands his office number out, but decides that his cell number would be a better alternative. Joe then leaves a quick message for Bills, "Hey uh, Bills it's Joe, I was thinking that maybe I could buy donuts for you and the service people at your next meeting. If that's OK just let me know when, thanks."

"OK Bobbi, I'm ready. Are you?" Joe asks as he holds his briefcase in his left hand and sips from his coffee cup with the other.

"Let me close up and I'm right there. Hey, where are we going today?" Bobbi asks as she bundles up her laptop and notepads. She decides to leave her overcoat on the hook. The radio said it was suppose to be a beautiful, sunny day with mild temperatures. She has always felt more professional with just her suit coat.

"There're a couple of places that I wanted to take you to. We've got a busy morning and we just cannot be late for the Carroll's appointment at 11:30. Bobbi, these probably won't be the best appointments for you to go on. I mean one is a billing issue and the other appointment is a new call for a fax machine. Not exactly exciting stuff you know?" Joe informs Bobbi as they walk through the now semi-empty office.

"Joe, I don't get a chance to spend enough time in the field. If I stay in my office, I'll get stuck doing busy work. This is a great opportunity to get out and leave all the administrative tasks behind, and besides it will let me be involved with customers. I too, need to become passionate again."

Joe questions, "Bobbi I thought you liked the administrative side to your job? You know the tracking and forecasting stuff."

"I hate paperwork," Bobbi responses emphatically. "If it wasn't for Louise keeping me straight I'd drown in paper. I do the shuffling because it is a requirement of my position, but I don't like it."

For the first time since Bobbi has been his manager, Joe feels that she has let her guard down a bit.

She has given him some sliver of information about herself that wasn't apparent. Maybe today wouldn't be as bad as he thought.

"I'll drive OK Bobbi?"

A few blocks from the office they stop at their first appointment. "Do I need to bring my briefcase or just a notepad?" she asks.

"I'm only going to be giving these revised invoices to them and I don't think you'll really need anything," Joe says, as he is about to lock the doors.

"Let me get my notepad, I feel awkward without something in my hands. It's as though I'm giving the impression to the customer that I'm not prepared. Or, that what they say doesn't really matter."

"Hi, I'm Joe Sails from Acme and this is Bobbi Dunham. Is Mike Faircloth available?"

The receptionist looks up and asks, "Is Mr. Faircloth expecting you?"

Knowing that Bobbi is watching Joe says, "Yes he is," and hands his business card to her, so that she can read his name. He then adds, "I talked with him yesterday afternoon."

Joe waits as Bobbi walks up to the desk, "Hi, Mr. Faircloth this is Jalynn at the front desk. There's a Mr. Sails from Acme here to see you. Yes sir, I'll send them right up."

"Mr. Sails, Mr. Faircloth will see you now. Please sign in over here." Joe picks up the pen and signs in for both himself and Bobbi.

In less than a minute they're walking into Mike Faircloth's office. He gets up from his desk and walks around the front to greet them. They meet halfway.

Joe smiles warmly and says, "Hi Mike, how are you?"

"Good, Joe."

"Mike, this is my boss, Bobbi Dunham. We're visiting customers together today and you were first on the list. I have those invoices for you."

"Great, come on in and have a seat," Mike says as he gestures easily to the two chairs in front of his desk. He is impeccably dressed and eases behind his desk into his chair. His shirt is starched and stiff, but his demeanor is very approachable. He folds his hands on top of his desktop calendar, smiles and waits.

Bobbi settles into a high back leather chair and notices that Mike's desk has few personal items except for some pictures, which she assumes, are of his family. Since she is at an angle to his desk and the pictures are also at an angle, she can only see a portion of the very furthest photograph. She quickly begins, "May I call you Mike? Thanks. I would like to personally apologize for any inconveniences that may have occurred based on our billing issues and to thank you for your time today."

"Thanks, but it may not have been all Acme's fault and it certainly wasn't your fault," he glances down at her card and then adds, "Bobbi."

"Thanks. It may sound a little cliché, but I am Acme. Every week, I get a check from Acme, so it is MY responsibility. I'd like to add that Joe is one of the most capable, customer-focused representatives that I have. You really are in good hands."

Mike doesn't refute anything that Bobbi says. He sits behind his desk and nods.

Joe then proceeds with the main purpose of the call, "Mike, I have copies of the bills right here and would like to go over them with you," Joe says.

"Sure."

Later as they are walking out the door, Bobbi adds, "Sometimes our bills are not as clear as they should be because of the nature of our business with monthly minimum charges and copy charges and then there's the possibility of overage charges. It can sometimes be very convoluted. If there are any further questions, please let us know."

"I do understand how difficult it can be to simplify billing yet produce accurate invoices. We sometimes have to deliver partial shipments or substituted products and that always causes billing nightmares," Mike says.

Joe's interest is piqued and he asks, "How do you work with your customers?"

"We do exactly what you're doing. We call or visit them. We try to minimize the issues by responding to them immediately."

"Do you mind if Joe calls you occasionally to discuss this further? Acme is benchmarking with customers on billing and supply chain issues."

Emphatically Mike answers, "Not at all. I can always find time to save time!" They shake hands again and promise to keep in close touch.

Joe is negotiating the last bit of rush hour traffic. "Bobbi, did you really mean that in there?" Joe asks as they're headed for their second appointment.

"Mean what?"

Joe explains a little shyly, "You know - that I'm extremely competent, and customer-focused, yada, yada, yada."

"Joe how long before we get to the next appointment?"

He answers, "Fifteen minutes," and thinks maybe she didn't hear him.

Bobbi decides that now is the time for brutal honesty. She starts off slowly, "Joe, do you know what your numbers have been for the last six months?"

Why is she asking me that? It certainly isn't an

answer to the question I asked, but he keeps from commenting negatively and says, "Not good Bobbi."

"I know they aren't good and I needed to do something. I believe your core competencies have changed for the worse. Six weeks ago, I made a decision to evaluate and elevate your core competencies."

"Bobbi, I'm not sure if I'm following you. What do you mean core competencies?"

Bobbi shifts in her seat. Her seatbelt is tugging at her shoulder. She is almost turned completely sideways, so she is facing Joe. "Good question. Let me explain it by telling you what it isn't first and then I'll give you a definition."

"It is not activity management. We manage today by activity reports and preset goals such as appointments, demos, proposals and eventually sales, right?" She doesn't stop to get a reply. "I will still set those goals for the team, but I have to be sure that each individual has core behaviors that will guide them through their daily tasks. These core behaviors cannot be quantified. They are the essence of how you do all aspects of our business and how you view yourself and your customers. Do you see where I'm going?"

"I'm not real sure," Joe says because he has never had this type of conversation with anyone before. All of his other managers have always stressed the results and the activities, 'Sales is a numbers game. See enough people and you'll eventually hit your number.' He honestly replies to Bobbi, "Are you talking about my closing capabilities?"

"No, I'm referring to something much more basic. I'm talking about your desire to do the right job or your driving force to get the job done right for the customer. There are a number of basic competencies that I view as critical for any successful salesperson; I don't care if they sell brushes door-to-door or software for GPS systems. In my view, these core behaviors are: a true empathy for the customer, attitude, taking responsibility, communications skills, which doesn't mean just the gift of gab, but accurate paperwork, emails, timely responses, etc. I also look for pride and the ability to adapt to new market pressures. There are obviously more, but for right now let's look at just a couple of the ones that I mentioned."

She pauses for two beats and continues. "I believe the market has changed and that you are now having difficulty adapting. You are still pushing boxes and not solutions. Your confidence is wavering and you're starting to develop bad habits. These habits have then turned into standard behaviors. Now you're three or four steps behind and it will only get worse."

"Let's take for example your workday. Since I have been monitoring and modifying your calendar, you have shown great improvement in the right activities, not just more hours. If you haven't noticed I was requesting that you solve billing issues first and then go on sales calls. Because all great salespeople would rather be selling then fixing problems. What I have done is scheduled your least favorable task first thing each morning to ensure that it gets done. Then the rest of the day is open for the things you like to do. Furthermore, by forcing you to address issues early, you were able to reduce the amount of time it takes to resolve them and maintain a customer's loyalty. I haven't allowed you to brush anything under the rug for almost the last two months."

"I wanted you to see that by staying on top of your customers' issues and not just pushing the problem to someone else, you truly have more time because your days are now not full of putting out fires. I've noticed that you haven't charged into my office lately demanding this or that."

"Bobbi, I haven't charged into your office because I felt that I was on thin ice."

Not conceding Bobbi challenges Joe, "Do me a favor and review your calendar for the last forty-five days and tell me all of the accounts that you have worked on. After that, look to see how many fires there have been. I'll bet there haven't been any real problems because you haven't come into my office yelling about them."

"OK let's say that you're right Bobbi. Now you have me working on problems all the time, but I still haven't sold my monthly quota," Joe says flatly. Last month the three "in stone" opportunities turned into only one actual order. He's not entirely convinced of Bobbi's arguments. He is relieved though. This thing wasn't a vendetta against him, but a program for improving him. "My numbers are flat and I can't seem to improve them."

"Hold on, let's backtrack a little. The idea is to work hard and smart. We need to have you get on the bus early and not have it run over you later. I wanted you to address customer issues early and not procrastinate on the ones you didn't WANT to work on. By forcing you to engage in customers' issues early, you save time. And every hour you save fighting fires is an hour more for sales. You are becoming more productive. Be honest, do you have more in your "Forecaster" now than you did four months ago?"

Begrudgingly Joe admits, "I guess."

"Anyway, how long are your typical sales, cycle-three months? Don't you think I went into this process knowing it would take three or four months for the results to show?"

Bobbi tries to explain it differently in a more

fundamental sense.   "Have you ever heard of the psychologist Pavlo?"

"No. I don't think so."

"He was a famous behaviorist who said that human behavior could be changed through rewards and punishments. One of his most renowned experiments dealt with a dog, Dr. Pavlov would ring a bell and then feed the dog. After a while the dog would salivate when the bell would ring even if a treat was not given. The rationale was that behavior could be modified through rewards, etc."

"Oh yeah, I remember that now," Joe comments.

Bobbi continues, "In my opinion, this is great logic for a one-dimensional dog, but the argument really doesn't hold true for salespeople because our rewards are more complex and may clearly be counterproductive. The most obvious reward for a salesperson is our compensation plan. But, there are other rewards that are much more subtle then money. If a sales rep cuts corners and gets to go home early, they may be rewarding themselves for bad behaviors. Or there may be a huge opportunity that they work on and they lose the business.   Since they don't get the reward-bonuses/ money, they may feel cheated or at the least frustrated. These feelings may cause them to change their behavior negatively.   They may stop working on big opportunities."

"I want to change core behaviors at their roots. This method, I believe, will change schedules and attitudes that reflect the right competencies. A solid foundation along with your sales skills can only equal success. Do you see where I'm going?" Bobbi asks.

"I think I do Bobbi, but I don't think my fundamentals are that bad, are they?"

"Before we pull in to the next appointment, let me

just say that the core behaviors are very difficult to manage. So there is no real end result or accomplishment. That being said, I doubt if anyone actually would offer that their core behaviors are bad because we all have a positive view of ourselves and maintain that image even if we have changed."

"Without cutting too close to the bone, I bet that you have an image of yourself that reflects your prior years' success. Furthermore, you have probably not accepted the fact that the last 12 months have been a bust. Right? Joe, we all have an image of ourselves that may not be perfectly accurate."

She finally answers his question and says, "I did mean what I said back there about you being very competent. And I do believe in the last six weeks that you have become more customer-focused. We just need to get the real Joe Sails back in the saddle again. I've started that process, not just by the calendar inspection, but also by having you travel with Bill Hamilton."

"So Bills was in on this the whole time?"

Bobbi, "No, not at all. Bill was NOT in on this. I thought he would be the one to exhibit the best examples of core competencies. When I asked him to travel with you he was excited about the idea because of your sales skills. So I think it was mutually beneficial."

Joe needs to think about this, so he's relieved to hear his cell phone ring. "Hello, this is Joe with Acme. How can I help you?"

It's Major Burnsides. "Joe, this is Major Burnsides. Is our meeting still on?"

"Yes sir, it is and I have all of the information that you requested. I'm going to be completely unbiased. I've got the digital information and some promotional prices on some of our older technologies, is that OK sir?"

"That's great. I'll see you at 10:00 sharp."

Joe adds, "Major because of your, actually our, I guess, security concerns, I'll be at your pass office at 9:30. Thanks again sir."

Chapter 9

the work has just begun

"Hello, is Ms. Kelsey Opportern in please?" Joe is holding the cell in the crux of his neck. He then says to Bobbi, "I'll ask Kelsey if we can still stop by this morning." Carroll's Food is their last scheduled appointment together for the day. It's 11:20 and Joe wants to confirm the appointment one more time.

After thinking about it, he does have to admit that all the traveling with Bobbi this morning has proven to be very productive. She is great in front of customers and very supportive of him to them. They have even uncovered some possible new requirements during the last appointment.

"Hi Kelsey, this is Joe with Acme. Are we still on for 11:30? Great, I'm only a few blocks away. I'll be on time and in your lobby in a flash." He sets his phone in a cubbyhole under his CD player. His cell is half charged, so he doesn't bother to plug it in.

"Sounds like we're set with Carroll's?" Bobbi inquires.

"Yup. That was Kelsey and she'll be there."

"Good. Can you give me an idea of what we're going to do?" Bobbi asks.

Joe almost blurts out, "Sell, sell and sell some more," but refrains and explains, "Bobbi, this is the second meeting with them and I would now normally be pressing for a trial or a demo. But, I don't think I want to discuss that now." Referring to their last call Joe says, "At Add-Right Accountants, you said some things that really made me think. You said, 'Anyone can sell a box, Acme sells solutions.' Well, I don't know what Carroll's real needs are because I have approached this account by only looking at what their current equipment is. If they've changed at all in the last four years since they bought all that old stuff then I may be creating problems for them. Look how much change Acme has gone through in the last four years. I'm sure Carroll's has changed just as much."

"So this call will be information gathering and trying to position ourselves as the long term solution providers. I may have come across in the first meeting as a copier salesman." Very sincerely and directly he adds, "I may need your help in a little damage control to get us back on track."

"This will be a piece of cake," Bobbi bolsters. "It's always easier to convince people in person than over the phone, and besides we haven't done anything wrong except for giving the image of limited capabilities. We've got the appointment; so let's paint the right picture. If you don't mind, I'll do that after the introductions, OK? I've been practicing my IBS dialogue on my commutes to and from work."

"Practicing? What do you mean practicing dialogue?" Joe's a little startled by this revelation. For the second time that morning his assumption of Bobbi as a number cruncher is shattered.

"Joe, I had a manager one time that said, 'the world is your canvas. It's up to you to paint the right picture.' He made me practice my Initial Benefits Statements all the time. If there were a new product I would have to give him an IBS. If there was a new vertical market we were going after, I would have to give him an IBS."

"You know, just verbalizing it makes me think that I've done an injustice to the team. I should have all of you give me introductory statements."

Joe says in jest, "I think I just made more work for myself."

"At least it's not more paperwork!" Bobbi easily banters back.

"What do you mean?"

Bobbi's excited and her words flow quickly, "I practice my initial customer statements while driving to work in the morning. I practice what I would say to a new customer, so that I convey confidence and competence while painting the correct picture of Acme. After several days of practice, I call my phone in the office and leave myself a message. Later on I listen to myself and make mental notes of how to improve."

"You do this every morning?" Joe's astonishment is evident.

"No, not every morning, just when new product lines or new software is introduced. I take it very seriously because you only have about 30 seconds of someone's attention to make the right first impression."

It's 11:30 on the dot when the receptionist asks, "Ms. Opportern, you have two guests in the lobby from Acme. OK, I'll have them sign in."

Joe bends slightly over the chest high counter when the receptionist hangs-up the phone and says, "You know the last time I was in here you knew I was from Acme. You must have a great memory."

"Thank you, but I review the senior managers'

schedules and note who is expecting whom," she confides.

"Well that's a great policy, and I'm thoroughly impressed."

She quickly adds, "It was my idea though, and now everyone does it." She hands them little badges the size of a playing card with their names on them.

Kelsey walks up just as they are pressing their new sticky badges on their lapels.

"Hi Kelsey, I'm happy that you could see us today." He extends his hand. "It's been awhile."

"Hi Joe. I know, I'm sorry. We've been very busy, but your timing is great."

"Kelsey, this is my boss, Bobbi Dunham."

"Hi, Bobbi my name's Kelsey Opportern and I am the director of purchasing. It's nice to meet you."

"Ms. Opportern, the pleasure is all mine."

"Please just call me Kelsey."

"Thanks and I'm really very interested in what Carroll's is doing. I know from some of the articles in the paper that the food service business is going through quite a change."

Joe recognizes that they are heading back toward the conference room where they had first met, the one with the huge solid cherry oval table. He is the last in line and has no trouble keeping up.

Kelsey turns her head slightly because she's leading their small group and says, "Bobbi, I see that you do your homework. I'm impressed."

"Thanks again, but actually Joe gets some credit. He told me about the account some time ago and I've just been keeping an eye on the paper." This is news to Joe because they hadn't even really talked at length about the market, let alone Carroll's Food and Beverage Wholesaler. He believes that it's prudent to shut-up and not disagree. Bobbi seems to be on a roll, but more importantly she's making him look good again.

As they enter the same conference room, the two gentlemen that were at the first meeting are there. They rise. Joe is thankful that he is at the end of the line because he has forgotten their names. Kelsey has already started the introductions. They all sit at the table. Bobbi immediately pulls her pen out and asks, "Before we begin, may I have the correct spelling of your last names along with your positions please?"

"Great," she captures their names and titles.

"I want to thank you again for your time. I know a little about your market, and a lillte about Carroll's Food and Beverage Wholesalers. Conversely, you probably know something about our business and only a little about Acme. I would like to first give you a broad overview of Acme. Then I could use a summary of Carroll's Food and Beverage Wholesalers and your particular requirements. Is that OK?"

Everyone nods his or her head in agreement.

"Great, Acme is an independent integrator of software and hardware solutions that provide our customers with solutions that increase productivity and decrease overall costs. Our expertise spans the digital environment from mainframe applications to LAN requirements. Furthermore, our philosophy and commitment to implementing open architecture solutions to satisfy customer requirements is our cornerstone to every strategic partnership." Bobbi waits. She hopes that the last statement wasn't too close to Carroll's mission statement for them to notice. Bobbi had reviewed their Website.

Preston is the first to speak and directs his question to Bobbi. "I'm glad that you succinctly described your organization. I was under the impression that most vendors in the office environment were pushing their copiers. Your comment about integration has me intrigued since I'm the IT Director. What types of integration does Acme do?"

"That's a good question. Acme takes the best software and hardware in the market places and unifies them. We typically look at data streams as they pertain to printing or viewing requirements. We are NOT a database management organization, but we work with them. We are not an ERP organization, but we work with them. Most of our customers have installed millions of dollars worth of hardware and software to streamline their organizations, but have neglected to consider document production. That is, the purpose of the information that they are gathering. This normally leads to bottlenecks or inefficient processing workflow."

"You may want to re-engineer your workflow and maybe even re-purpose the information for maximum utilization."

Bobbi stops for a brief moment. When she begins, she seems to have lost her momentum and appears a little scatterbrained. "You know rush hour traffic is crazy around here. It sometimes takes me over an hour to go less than seven miles. Everyone has his or her own car and it just gets worse every year. If they widen the roads, we use them more and traffic increases. Even if I buy a faster car, let's say a Lamborghini, I'll still spend the same amount of time in rush hour traffic if I don't change my way to work or workflow."

She nails it. Everyone around the table is smiling and nodding. They're getting it.

"Let's view your network as rush hour traffic. Furthermore, let me ask one quick question as clarification. Do most of your employees now have a printer connected to their computers and are there copiers all over the place?"

Kelsey, "You seem to have touched the root issue within our company. We can't seem to get our arms around our SAG expenses."

Two and a half hours later, Bobbi and Joe are at their favorite deli enjoying a late lunch. Of course Joe's having ham and Swiss on rye while Bobbi is enjoying another Caesar salad. Joe has the sports page open and Bobbi is reading the business section.

Joe looks up and says, "I can't believe we didn't talk at all about our products the entire time in their office. That was a great call!"

"Joe, we talked about what their real issues are, not what everyone else thinks their issues are. We painted a picture big enough of Acme to let them respond to us. We need to stop focusing on our solutions and start focusing on the customer's problems and how they affect their critical business requirements."

"I see your point Bobbi. I don't think I would have done this your way if I hadn't seen you in action. Oh, by the way, I would really like for you to travel with me next week to the Army National Guard. How's your schedule look?"

"I'm not sure, but let's talk about it when we get back to the office," she says.

Joe flips the pages of the newspaper and starts to read about his Cougars. Bobbi is lost in thought about core competencies again. If she has been so busy tracking results, has she lost some of her own core competencies? Who is going to show her what is a good example of management core competencies? She's gone to management school, but that's a joke when you're in the real world. You really only learn how to activity-manage and how to avoid lawsuits. She may possess core skills, but she's sure there are many that are being overlooked. How does she improve? Has anyone ever discussed this with her? Of course they haven't. Profitability, headcount and revenues are used to measure her. This whole idea of core competencies is so elusive that she feels she may be constantly striving for a non-existent goal.

Then she looks at Joe and the improvement he has made in such a short time and she's certain her logic and rationale are sound. There's more work to be done, but he's off to a good start. He's seems to have righted himself and hopefully the bad weather is behind him.

Bobbi truly believes that managing is like sailing. You constantly have to be monitoring all conditions to be running a tight ship.

ooooooooooooooooo

Words from the author:

I truly hope that this book has helped you to consider your own core competencies. If you challenged yourself while reading this story you are already halfway there. Self-improvement is a constant effort, but realization is the first step. True cultural change cannot take place without individuals changing.

This is not a book to be shelved. It is meant to be shared. Please sign and pass it to a friend or coworker.

Dick Olenych

I invite your thoughts and comments.
dick@joesails.info

ooooooooooooooooo

ooooooooooooooo

Signatures and comments:

ooooooooooooooo

oooooooooooooooo

Signatures and comments:

oooooooooooooooo